CW00739272

'Is There Anybody There?' said the Traveller

MULLER

BY THE SAME AUTHOR

Novels

The Feathers of Death
Brother Cain
Doctors Wear Scarlet
Close of Play
The Roses of Picardie
An Inch of Fortune
September Castle

Alms For Oblivion sequence

Fielding Gray
Sound the Retreat
The Sabre Squadron
The Rich Pay Late
Friends in Low Places
The Judas Boy
Places Where They Sing
Come Like Shadows
Bring Forth the Body
The Survivors

Belles-Letters

The English Gentleman
Boys Will Be Boys
The Fortunes of Fingel
The Old School

Plays

Royal Foundation and Other Plays

Autobiography

Shadows on the Grass
The Old Gang
Bird of Ill omen

The First Born of Egypt sequence

Morning Star
The Face of the Waters
Before the Cock Crow
New Seed For Old
Blood of My Bone
In The Image of God

'IS THERE ANYBODY THERE?' SAID THE TRAVELLER

Memories of a Private Nuisance

Simon Raven

FREDERICK MULLER

LONDON SYDNEY AUCKLAND JOHANNESBURG

© Simon Raven 1990
The right of Simon Raven to be identified as Author of this
work has been asserted by Simon Raven in accordance with the
Copyright, Designs and Patent Act, 1988

All rights reserved

This edition first published in 1990 by
Frederick Muller, an imprint of
Century Hutchinson Ltd
20 Vauxhall Bridge Road, London SW1 2SA

Century Hutchinson Australia (Pty) Ltd
20 Alfred Street, Milsons Point, Sydney NSW 2061

Century Hutchinson New Zealand Limited
PO Box 40–086, Glenfield, Auckland 10, New Zealand

Century Hutchinson South Africa (Pty) Ltd
PO Box 337, Bergvlei, 2012 South Africa

British Library Cataloguing in Publication Data

Raven, Simon, *1927–*
    Is there anybody there? said the traveller
    I. Title
    823.514

    ISBN 0–09–174 398–2

Typeset by Deltatype Ltd, Ellesmere Port
Printed and bound in Great Britain by
Mackays of Chatham

THE LISTENERS

'Is there anybody there?' said the Traveller,
   Knocking on the moonlit door;
And his horse in the silence champed the grasses
   Of the forest's ferny floor:
And a bird flew up out of the turret,
   Above the Traveller's head:
And he smote upon the door again a second time;
   'Is there anybody there?' he said.
But no one descended to the Traveller:
   No head from the leaf-fringed sill
Leaned over and looked into his grey eyes,
   Where he stood perplexed and still.
But only a host of phantom listeners
   That dwelt in the lone house then
Stood listening in the quiet of the moonlight
   To that voice from the world of men:
Stood thronging the faint moonbeams on the dark stair,
   That goes down to the empty hall,
Hearkening in an air stirred and shaken
   By the lonely Traveller's call.

Walter de la Mare

Old men do *not* forget, but their memories do a lot of editing, especially in respect of the deeds, and the misdeeds, which they did on the bright fields of their youth. Good becomes heroic; bad becomes at worst tolerable – unless, of course, it is somebody else's bad and therefore legitimate prey to the septic inquisition of malice. (Come to that, other people's good doesn't come off too well either.)

And yet, for all one's exaggeration or distortion of what occurred in one's youth, memories of that time are curiously precise, often eliciting tiny details and endowing them with all the brilliance of form and colour of a meadow flower in a medieval painting. I can still remember the exact position I was in when I held an important catch at deep leg, to dismiss PDS Blake, Captain of the Eton XI, on Green at Charterhouse in the June of 1945: I snatched at the ball with a panicky clap of the hands when it was a foot above the ground and about to strike the shinbone of my left and leading leg, a loathsome performance, as any half-way educated cricketer will tell you. But the ball stuck and this, added to other fluky feats, procured me my colours, and I have remembered the split second of impact and the almost hysterical surge of joy ever since.

Very old memories, then, are intense and vivid; but they are quite as vivid about what never happened as about what did. I can check that I caught out Blake that summer afternoon because I still have a copy of a printed record (in *The Carthusian*) of the match; so about that my memory must be correct. But it is somewhat at fault when it conjures a picture, equally clear, of my sitting knee-to-urgently-responding-knee with a member of the XI with whom I was much infatuated, and of our together applauding PBH May when he came in at the close of the Charterhouse innings at Harrow that same June, having made 150 not out. The record, this time to be found in Wisden itself (1946 edition), states that May was 'c. Blackwell b. Arnott 77'. If I imagined Peter's century and a half, did I also imagine the sweet, sweaty pressure of Eros' flannelled thigh?

So at forty years on one's memories are brilliant but misleading. At twenty years on, I find, they are perhaps more accurate but far less moving, dramatic, or erotic, even when they are of matters that were of great pith and moment at the time. Joy and sorrow are not there, as they are in visions of the earlier times: there is only a grinding sequence of the events that actually took place. For example: when I recall sitting with Eros in his pink blazer on that bench on the boundary at Harrow, my heart still rises (and never mind what really happened); but when I think of a far more passionate, more loving and more authentic episode shortly after my forty-third birthday, all I see is a dull concurrence and regression of limbs bleakly etched in black and white. Forty, I suppose, is a prosaic age and memories of the period correspondingly literal.

Memories of recent events should, of course, be the most reliable of all. But in my own case, being those of a man on the edge of old age (62), they are rendered less so by spite and spleen; by envy, resentment and sulk.

Pray, gentle reader, bear these admissions in mind while you peruse, should you have the leisure and patience, the pages that follow. For this is a work of comparison: how did such a place, such a poem or such a picture, such a pastime or (above all) such a person seem to one when one was in one's salad days? then again, at the age of forty and during the middle years that succeeded it? or yet again, at sixty when there remain (so the scribe admonishes us) only ten good years to run? This exercise must depend on memory: so make allowance, of your charity, for the bitterness which the author may exude when writing of the immediate past; the self-satisfied yet cynical calculus which he may tend to apply to his maturity, and the facile indulgence with which, as vanity or discretion may dictate, he puffs the gallantry or palliates the shame of his spunky youth.

Simon Raven
Walmer, 23 July 1990

PART ONE

Flower Of The Peach

Flower o' the peach,
Death for us all, and his own life for each!

Robert Browning; *Fra Lippo Lippi: 11. 248 and 249*

'The peacock,' said Benjamin Crud, 'is the symbol of wisdom.'

'I had thought,' I said, 'that it was the symbol of vanity.'

We were examining a bas-relief in the iconostasis of the cathedral at Torcello on Midsummer's Eve of 1987.

'Not in the eleventh century. The peacock in those days was taken to be more than merely wise: it was considered to be omniscient.'

'I have been told,' I said, 'that before the war we had peacocks in the courts of my college. All they ever did was to drive people potty with their abominable squawk.'

'They were proclaiming their splendour and importance,' Benjamin said. 'You see, for a start, the flesh of the peacock was deemed to be incorruptible — '

'Why — ?'

' — A good question,' said Benjamin Crud, brandishing his Hebrew nose like a scimitar. 'Presumably because either they were killed and gobbled up by rodents, or they were eaten at banquets by human beings *or* they concealed themselves very cleverly and modestly if they knew that they were about to die of natural causes. In any of these cases, their cadavers, their dead flesh, would never be seen to decay. Nor was it. Hence their reputation for never decomposing.'

'Good effort,' I applauded. 'Intelligent Americans are the most plausible people I know. Intelligent Europeans are so aggressive and assertive that they are intolerable. Very well, then: let us accept that the flesh of peacocks is incorruptible; why does that make them omniscient?'

'Because they are believed to be a type of the resurrection. This means that they live forever and therefore have the time to accumulate knowledge . . . all knowledge. Furthermore, they are, of course, holy. "By the Peacock" was once a formidable oath.'

'Christian or pagan, Benj?'

For unknown reason Benjamin preferred this abominable vocative to 'Benjamin' in full or either of the two other available contractions, 'Ben' or 'Benjie'.

'Christian. To the pagans, the peacock was only a beautiful *vanitas* creature – Hera's favourite attendant, if you remember – and Hera was not an edifying character even to pagans.'

'Nor were any of the immortal gods, with the possible exception of Athena. And even she has been painted by an Italian artist of merit having her tits and thighs fondled by her father, Zeus. It was their moral fallibility that made the gods so popular in classical times and ever since.'

'I think,' said Benj, 'that they had a serious side.'

We turned and walked down to the Mosaic of The Last Judgment on the west wall.

'It rather depended,' Benj continued as we went, 'on who was writing about them. Homer did their repute no good, but Virgil gave them a bit of a boost.'

'I thought no one in America read Homer or Virgil any more.'

'Oh but we do – in English.' He paused. 'Anyway, as you very well know, my own tastes are entirely European. The trouble is that I'm now so European that I find my innocence has been destroyed. I am now obsessed by the vileness of the human race.'

'Had you remained in America you might not have noticed it?'

'Something of the sort. I am also overwhelmed by the vileness of *myself*. I can just see myself among that lot there being tortured in Hell.'

'Literally?' I said.

'Almost.'

I inspected the torments that were going on.

'You can't really see yourself in that gallery?'

'Almost,' Benj repeated dismally.

'You . . . you actually mean it,' I said.

'Guilt, dear boy: guilt. Last autumn, while alone and very low with influenza, I had a terrifying vision of all the sins I had committed throughout the sixty-odd years of my life. It was like that procession of the future kings of Scotland in *Macbeth* – only in my case it was a procession of past crimes, past enormities, that padded inexorably towards me . . . along the bottom of a ravine so narrow that I was held fast by the rock on either side and unable to move in any direction, so deep that at its summit only the thinnest streak of sky, no broader than a thread of cotton, was visible. Although the ravine was so strait, I somehow had the power to look right along the whole procession, and what I saw made me sweat and tremble with despair. Could it really have been I, Benjamin Crud, that had behaved with such lust and cruelty and greed, that had created the monsters which were gliding between the walls of adamant towards me?'

'You imagined it.'

'Of course I did. And kept on imagining it. How was I to be saved from my vision of Hell?'

Crud took me by the arm and hustled me the length of the cathedral to the east end, where was another Mosaic, this one of Mary weeping. 'Only by pity and forgiveness,' he said: 'such as we see here.'

'Where were you,' I said, 'when the first attack of these horrors happened?'

'In Brussels.'

'And where did you find . . . pity and forgiveness . . . in Brussels?'

'One day, as I walked through the picture gallery, I came upon a really disgusting picture by Hieronymus Bosch of professional executioners engaged in whipping and defiling Christ. Their faces were as hideous as their spiked and jagged implements. These men were my sins, I thought. But the Christ who was being tortured by them, although his face was rippling and shimmering with pain, looked at them with forgiveness. With pity. For He knew how they must hate themselves as well as Him. There was peace for me in that picture, in the same way as there is in this Mosaic of Mary shedding her huge tear for, among others, me.'

'But,' I said, 'you are incapable of such deeds as you describe. While you are occasionally mean about money, you are not, on the whole, given to greed . . . or to cruelty . . . or even lust.'

'Only I can know that, and I know the worst. I said just now that the pagan gods had a serious side to them, but I do not think that forgiveness or pity was prominent in their repertoire. Acts of casual generosity, yes: but for the forgiveness that could lift a man out of the pit that I was in I needed Christ and His Mother.'

'So the pale Galilean has conquered you too?' I said.

We walked out of the cathedral, down the roofed passage, across the meadow, and then along the bleak, reedy margin of the scummy canal.

'The problem is,' said Benj, 'how to guarantee that the power of Christ and Mary will operate on my behalf and save me from the shadow.'

'It already has. Their images have freed you from your vision of Hell.'

'Their images have freed me from a vision. One day I shall need their real essence to free me from the real Hell.'

'You honestly believe in that?'

'No. Not quite. Not yet. But I am getting nearer to believing in it. I must . . . assemble the means for my protection. I must — ' he grinned at me ' — take out the proper insurance. No firm like the old firm: the Roman Catholic Church. Other versions of the faith perhaps preceded it in the early Christian days, others have come and gone, conquered and been submerged. But the Roman Catholic Church is still with us.'

'What about Judaism? You were born to it, after all.'

'Judaism does not much concern itself with the immortal soul. Most Jews don't even believe in it.'

'Judaism concerns itself with righteousness.'

'It does not offer secure guarantees. It is too shifty and oriental and fatalistic. Give me the old firm, Simon: the Roman Catholic Life Assurance – or rather Death Assurance. Give me its policy against Damnation.'

'I am told that the old firm's premiums come exceedingly high for rich and frightened old faggots . . . both in the world's currency and in the quality of repentance required.'

'I have not yet,' said Benjamin Crud, 'fully decided to pay them. This loathing of myself may wear off. Lighter and brighter counsels may prevail. I shall take a few more months before I commit myself. Meanwhile, please stop me if I become boring on the subject. There is no bore so deadly as a religious bore.'

'Very well,' I said. 'Tonight is Midsummer's Eve. A pagan celebration is in order and may restore your good spirits.'

'I doubt it very much,' snuffled Benj.

We walked back to the meadow under the cathedral and then along the raised path that led, by another and slightly less noisome canal, to Torcello's landing stage.

'You know,' I said, 'your description of that Bosch painting reminds me of the hoteliers and restaurateurs of Venice . . . their whole bodies misshapen with avarice. They used not to be like that. But now their heads over their account books are like maces with rusty studs and their hands like twisted implements of torture as they reach for one's traveller's cheques.'

'Like the hands and faces I saw in that ravine,' said Crud: 'like my own face and hands, come to that. I have a feeling that mere likenesses of Christ and Mary, sculpted or painted, will not be enough to heal me; that I shall need the confidence that comes only from being insured by the old firm.'

'You said you were going to wait some months more.'

'Don't worry,' said Benj. 'I certainly shan't join the Church here in Venice. The churches here are very beautiful, but such priests as I have observed in them flitter about like black Harpies, hissing and snatching like the whores in the Piazza.'

'I see that there is an exhibition,' said Michael Webb, 'called "The Plague in Venice". Perhaps it will keep away tourists.'

'No such luck,' I said.

We were having lunch *al fresco* at Harry's Restaurant by the meadow on Torcello: Michael Webb, who was a scholar of Byzantine Greek and a friend of my dead brother, like him a prep schoolmaster; two of his colleagues, one bald and one musical; and myself.

'It's still only April,' said Michael's bald colleague, Matthew, 'and still Low Season, I hope, when it comes to computing hotel bills.'

'Low Season,' I said glumly, 'is now a thing of the past. The whole year is Full Season and has been for two years now, since 1977. The Venetians get greedier every week. And it's no good hoping that anything will keep away tourists. Venice, as a certain kind of journalist says, will run and run.'

'"Until at last it runs right over,"' said Michael, 'as the rude song has it.'

'The Monks of San Giorgio Maggiore,' said David, his musical colleague, 'still sing in Latin. They are doing a Requiem Mass this evening. It might be apposite to go to the exhibition about the Plague and then attend the Mass.'

'Not good form,' I grumbled. 'We can't possibly know the chap it's for. Anyhow, I haven't brought a black tie or a suitable suit.'

'No, no, no,' said bald Matthew. 'You buy a ticket for this Mass. It's not a real Requiem, only make-believe.'

'Show biz,' said Michael: 'like everything else in Venice.'

'At least,' said David, 'this food is genuine.'

'It's too expensive to be anything else,' I said, 'even in Venice. Make the most of it.'

'Willingly. A chap needs nourishing for Plague followed by Requiem,' said Matthew, 'even if they are only show biz.'

The ferry from Torcello via Mazzorbo and Murano to Venice was crowded with English children on a school expedition. The teacher in charge had hair nearly down to the pelvis; he wore grey gym shoes, ripped jeans, and a shirt which announced 'Love, Lovely Love' for all creeds, colours and sexes. An assistant teacher wore pretty well identical garments but was to be distinguished by short cropped hair, though which style indicated which sex was uncertain, as both brandished bangles and neither sported teets. Their pupils (if one is still permitted to use the word) were cheerful clowns and hoydens who amused themselves by slobbering on each other's faces and feeling each other up across the aisle between the seats until gently discouraged by a tourist policeman, after which they directed their healthy energies to chanting obscenities at the Italian passengers. Most of them lit up, cupping their weeds in their palms like delinquent soldiers enjoying 'a crafty snout' on sentry duty. Two individualists stood out: an overgrown but comely girl who wept incessantly (thwarted love?) and a very pretty little boy who had both hands rammed down the front of his pocketless trousers and frotted away frenetically and (it would appear) with no success at all during the entire half-hour of our journey

10

to the Fondamenta Nuove. Surely these two might have been brought together? Their teachers ignored their plight and concentrated on maintaining sullen yet righteous expressions, which proclaimed that they were not ashamed of their charges and woe betide anyone who complained of them. Even the courteous tourist-cop had been pursued by a hiss of 'Fascist bastard' from one of the unisex educators.

'I think it must be part of a left-wing conspiracy,' said Michael Webb, 'to discredit England abroad. I once saw a similar party in Diocletian's Palace in Split. Those were rather younger children, one of whom had a very splashy public piddle on the floor of the vestibule.'

'You could be right,' said Matthew, 'but surely any left-wing movement would have wished to send a well-behaved and attractive party to a communist country like Yugoslavia?'

'To other communist countries perhaps, but not, it seemed, to Yugoslavia. The teaching person in charge was heard to say, very loudly and several times, that the private profiteering of the inhabitants along the Dalmatian Coast was a disgrace to socialism.'

'Well,' said David, 'I don't suppose that this lot will be coming to The Plague in Venice Exhibition.'

He should have known better. The title of the exhibition had caught the children's fancy and although they eschewed the records and documents, they adored the paintings of people who were displaying their royal purple buboes adjacent to their bulky if usually concealed *privata*. The hermaphroditic guardians railed at a curator who turned one of the older girls out of his official chair, and the frotting boy emitted a high wail, though whether this indicated despair or well-deserved fulfilment was uncertain. Otherwise it can fairly be said that the school party did little to affront the other patrons of the exhibition, had indeed enriched the occasion by artless comments – 'Our Ron had a bluebottle like thut on his bum' (to rhyme with womb).

'At least,' said David, as they trailed away across the piazza, leaving a spoor of peel and cellophane, 'they won't be coming to the Requiem Mass at San Giorgio.'

Nor did they – except for the large, weeping girl, who came alone and was much comforted by the glum and sonorous music; so cheered was she that before long she began to sniff instead of cry, to giggle instead of sniff, to laugh instead of giggle, and finally to vibrate in outright hysteria, at which stage she was led away by a corvine verger.

'She was perfectly right to laugh,' said David, the musician, after the show. 'None of those dreadful old men could sing for macaroni. They charged us ten thousand lire each – and didn't even perform in their own beautiful chancel. Why do you suppose we all had to be crammed into that smelly chapterhouse?'

'We were being punished,' said Michael the Byzantine, 'for treating an office of Christian worship like an operatic entertainment.'

'At their invitation.'

'But at our penance. At least we were allowed on to the island. Last time I was here, there was a conference of politicians and economists in the old monastic buildings. People like Mrs Thatcher came to it. None of the public was allowed off the ferry – there was about a battalion of police on the quay to stop us disembarking. Politicians should confer in places which suit their so called aspirations, like Frankfurt or Lisle or Birmingham. Nobody half-way decent could get into the church for five whole days.'

Just as the attendant sailor was about to cast off the ferry, the large girl from the school party was hustled on deck and left there by the corvine verger from the chapterhouse. He seemed very relieved to be rid of her, and almost ran across the stone flags of the church and up the steps into sanctuary.

The girl had finished both with tears and laughter. She was bovine, cowed.

'Are you all right?' said Michael.

'Oh yes. Ta.'

'What happened? What did that old man in black say to you?'

'Didn't say nothun much. Knew nowt English. Took us to an office. Kept squawkin' "'Ostel, 'ostel, 'ostel." So I reckons he wants the name of the hostel us be in, and since he can't understand when us tells him, I writes it down. Then he looks in a telephone book, and after a lot of cluckin' an' clackin' he rings up and talks to someone, and seems summat relieved, and says, "You to go now; you to go now; there, there, there" – pointin' with a finger like a spike at the name I'd written down. So I gives him the nod, but he still insist on comin' down to ferry-boat, clutchin' us all the way. And here we be.'

'Yes,' said David, pushing up his spectacles and letting them drop back on to the bridge of his nose, 'here you be. We saw you earlier in the day, you know. You didn't look as if you were enjoying yourself. You were crying all the time.'

'Yus. Because nor Sir nor Miss would explain these luvly things we're seein'. They won't even tell us where to get guidebook. Truth is, Sir and Miss is hating this trup. Sir and Miss wanted fer to go with the trup to Romania, but they was told off to cum wuth us here. They don't like the place. They don't appruv. No fuctories, no housin' estates to look at – all of it too old for 'em, too perdy and too old. They only takes us to see the churches and things in case they gets reported; not that any of the kids would tell, 'cos they wouldn't care what they saw 'slong they can kuss and cuddle, but I s'pose the Italian warden at the hostel might peach on 'em. So I'se crying because of the waste. All these luvly things and nobody won't tell me nowt about them. Thut weird great church on Torcello island, thuz paintings in that dark place – nuthun. They knows nuthun, Sir nor Miss, nor wants to.'

'How did you get to the Requiem?'

'There wuz a notice in the hostel, so I ask the warden man in charge and he gives me a tuckut for the concert and a pass for the boat. Tells me how to walk down to Rialto Bridge and catch a bus-boat and then catch another from near the palace.'

'Why,' said David, 'did you find the performance so funny?'

'I likes the music. But them old duddies couldn't sing, poor old clouns. I sings in the choir at home. Us knows a note from another. But I've had a nice time, on my own.'

The vaporetto deposited us near the Danieli.

'Where is your hostel?' Matthew said. 'We'll walk you there.'

The hostel was near the Youth Centre in the old Scuola della Misericordia. So we proceeded there by easy stages, showing the girl the Bellini Madonna in San Zaccaria, the façade of San Zanipolo (the church itself being closed), the Gesuiti (also closed – but is it ever open?), and, as we approached the hostel, the distant Casino degli Spiriti. She enjoyed Michael's description of the gatherings there at which scholars read and discussed the Dialogues of Plato. It was the last thing she did enjoy that evening. Both unisex teachers were waiting at the entrance to the hostel. They each took one of the girl's arms,

13

glared at all of us as though about to accuse us of gang-rape, then snatched her inside.

'Thank you, gen'lmen,' the girl called. 'It was real ki — '

But by then the teacher with the cropped hair had clapped a hand over her mouth.

'Since we are in this quarter,' I said, 'we might try dinner at that very curious hotel, the one named after the Madonna dell' Orto. More or less in the ghetto.'

Thither we went, halting briefly in the little campo in front of the sinister crepuscular façade of the Church of Our Lady of the Vegetable Garden ('Orto' having nothing much to do with flowers).

'We never asked that girl her name,' Matthew said heavily.

We trailed on to the hotel. The restaurant was closed. We had a drink in the garden, a wilderness of head-high scrub, through which a path led to the shore of the lagoon, giving a grand view of the Island of the Cemetery.

'This is called the Isola San Michele,' said Michael mirthlessly.

'If we go straight down towards the Grand Canal,' I said, 'we shall come to the Palazzo Vendramin, where the gaming rooms operate in winter.'

'Where Wagner died,' said David.

'Not before time,' said Matthew.

'From there,' I persisted, 'we can get a boat to the Rialto Bridge. At the Rialto there are many places to eat.'

'That poor girl has killed my appetite,' David said.

'Nothing kills my appetite,' said Michael: 'I feel like a particularly elaborate dinner to make up for those dismal monks and that eponymous charnel establishment.'

'Then we shall go to the Graspo da Ua,' I said: 'it's only a step from the Rialto, and I believe it has a rosette in the Italian *Michelin*.'

Thirty years before, the first time I came to Venice, the Ristorante Al Graspo da Ua had not had a rosette. In those days there was no Italian *Michelin*. How very much better off we were without it, neither misled by obsolete reports nor jostled by those foolish enough to believe them.

'*Dovè andiamo per fare il pranzo?*' I had said carefully and, as I still

14

think, correctly, to the auburn girl whom I had seen at her prayers in the Church at Santa Maria Formosa a few minutes before seven o'clock.

'If you know the way, as I do,' she said in soft but slightly nasal English, 'it is not far to the Graspo da Ua. You realise, of course, that I am for money. Otherwise I should not be alone. I was praying to the Madonna to be forgiven before I started my work of the evening. It has begun sooner than I had hoped, and more kindly. People do not often ask me to dinner first.'

'I am hungry,' I said.

'So am I.'

During dinner, for which she had both appetite and taste, the auburn girl told me how she had become a prostitute, a dull tale, typical of the decade after the ending of the war, and of her fortune during the three months she had been engaged in the profession.

'I have had illness,' she said, with unaffected candour over the *carne*. 'Twice. The little illness, thanks to God.'

'One wouldn't know,' I said sincerely.

'With the little illness you cannot tell, until you see the fluid from the labia. That is why so many people get the little illness – it is passed on to them by girls who do not know they have it. Even the great illness is not visible in girls, until the later stages. I can promise you, thanks to Our Lady, I have neither the small nor the big illness at this time.'

'You have regular tests?'

'I have a doctor who treats me free. When I am all right, he goes with me in his surgery. So I always hope that he will go with me . . . Unfortunately, the second time of the little illness has made me dry. Although it was some weeks ago, I am still dry.'

'Dry?'

'Dry where I should be wet. But I am still warm there. If you are strong and stiff, it will not matter.'

In those days I was strong and stiff. Three times that night I was strong and stiff: the first time she mounted me and groaned '*Madonna, Madonna*' as she came. Or was she just groaning at the nuisance and discomfort of it all? True, her belly rippled and juddered, but any girl can make her belly do that with a little practice. I don't think, however, that she was shamming, because it was she who initiated the second

15

round (missionary position) and then woke me for a third (*a tergo sed non per anum*). Why should she have roused me, reluctant as I was, for the third bout if she had not wanted it? It is always possible, of course, that her professional conscience instructed her that she must give full value, whatever the disposition of her client. She was an odd enough girl for that – odd enough, too, to give me credit until the next morning, for the Graspo had grasped cruelly (no credit cards in 1951) and by the time I had paid the night's lodging in the Pensione Doge (in advance, I need hardly say), I had almost nothing.

Apart from having to ask the auburn girl for credit, which I was old enough to know was not popular with practitioners in her line, there were two other embarrassments. So strict was security in Italy (and still is) even in *maisons de passe*, that the Doge insisted I should produce my passport, which meant going back to my official hotel, the Gabrielli Sandwirth, to fetch it. In those days the Gabrielli was only a pensione but a good deal more reputable than the Doge, certainly not welcoming the casual visits of auburn girls, and getting in and out after nine-thirty was definitely a production. Why, enquired the po-faced Swiss proprietor, did I want my passport? To go to the casino on the Lido, I lied. With a wrathful frown he handed the thing over: I should remember, he said, that if I was not back by eleven I should not be able to get in again until six-thirty in the morning. That, of course, was not a problem though waking up in the Doge brought the second embarrassment – workers on the roof of St Mark's peering straight through our open window. (The girl shared my English taste for fresh air: 'Love can make a lot of smell,' she had said the previous night.) 'How lucky,' she grinned now, 'that we were so – how do you say? – hygienic.' Whereupon she waved to the workers and started to set up a fourth *parti*. Ah well, I thought, the day is too beautiful and the sky too blue for any footling bourgeois inhibitions; and I joined her with a will in the canine version of *a tergo* (as opposed to the lateral mode which she had favoured the previous night). Then the bells began to ring. 'Boom-boom, boom-boom,' chanted the workers, merrily masturbating.

'*Madonna, Madonna, Madonna, Madonna mi-i-i-i-a,*' squealed the auburn girl: 'just look at those beautiful big brown peegoes.' (Where could she have learned that quaint and obsolete term?) So she did and I did. '*Maria, Maria, Maria, gratia pleeeena,*' she screeched, while I crushed out the last lovely drops and still quaked in seismic ecstasy.

In order to get the girl's well-earned money I had to take my traveller's cheques to a bank. Would she like to come too? No, she said trustingly: she would meet me in Harry's Bar for a drink in half an hour.

When I arrived she was drinking coffee. I gave her the agreed five thousand lire. Would I care, she asked, to meet her again that evening? Not possible, I said, drained by *coitus*, thinking of the casino, which I had called into my thoughts by my lie to the proprietor of the Gabrielli the night before. Ah well, she said. I knew where to find her if ever I wanted her: between six-thirty and seven o'clock in the Chiesa Santa Maria Formosa. She always said her prayers in the same place. '*Ci'ao.*'

Having had no breakfast, I helped myself to what I took to be a free prawn sandwich from a plate of appetisers which one of the barmen was handing round. The sandwich, I soon discovered, cost ten times as much as the coffee. But by then I had something else to sadden me. I had at no stage, I now remembered, asked this sweet, randy, trusting girl's name . . . nor she mine, come to that, being quite content with '*caro*'. Well, I thought: the whole point of having prostitutes is the convenient anonymity. At least I had been civil enough to buy her dinner.

I won some handy money in the spring and summer casino on the Lido, but was conned out of a substantial sum some three days later, by an American sailor boy, pneumatic and juicy, who said he needed forty thousand lire to see him through a tedious sequence of Saints' Days and would repay me *fifty* thousand when the banks reopened. Thus having roused my greed, he left me a roll of cloth as security. I waited three hours for him in the appointed café before taking the roll to the proprietor of the Gabrielli, who sanctimoniously pronounced it worthless. Luckily I had paid him money in advance from my roulette win, in order to have the pleasure of telling him where the money came from, but I still had to go home early. I should have stuck to the warm, dry auburn girl from the Santa Maria Formosa.

*

On Christmas Day, if you want to go to Torcello, you must do so in a private boat. In 1969 this was still quite inexpensive, particularly if somebody else was paying. Hamilton Glott, the publicity man, wasn't paying; nor was his friend Hamish M'cSass, the blond beauty with the tantalising touch of the tar-brush; nor my son, Adam, still only sixteen years old; nor my military friend, 'O', who didn't see why he should when richer people were present; nor I, for the same reason. Martin Stevens, the globular aspirant politico, picked up the ticket, because he was generous and liked everyone to know it.

On Torcello, only the Cathedral of Santa Maria Assunta was open. Harry's Restaurant did not open in the depths of winter; nor does it now, although winter, however deep, these days counts as Full Season.

On the way over the meadow to the cathedral, Adam said, 'Can we go up that tower?'

'The campanile?' I said. 'No.'

'Ruskin did,' said Martin.

'That was before people were made to pay to be interfered with in places like this.'

'I wish someone would interfere with me,' said Martin. 'It's very dreary out here.'

'So melancholy,' said Adam, the apprentice artist; 'and beautiful.'

'I've left my cigarettes behind,' said Hamilton Glott.

'And your money, I suppose,' said Hamish M'cSass. 'I'm not going to pay for your lunch, you know.'

'Where shall we find any lunch?' said O.

'All your money is really mine,' said Hamilton to Hamish. 'If you don't pay for my lunch, I'll chuck you out.'

'I'll take you on,' said Martin, 'beginning now, behind the campanile.'

'You can't afford him,' I said.

'Ah,' Martin said. He paid for us all to enter the cathedral, led us to The Last Judgment in the west wall, and began an oration:

'Tel-Hotel,' Martin announced. 'The big buy of the nascent Seventies. You are at an airport at two a.m., you want to book yourself into an hotel, but you don't know the city and you don't fancy being driven all round it in the dark by a swindling taxi driver and being

18

refused at place after place. So what do you do? You see in front of you a Tel-Hotel machine, and on inserting a small coin — '

' — Just what you wouldn't have,' said Adam, 'in a new country at two in the morning.'

'On inserting a small coin, you read on a screen a list of all the hotels that have vacancies. On insertion of another small coin — '

' — Which you wouldn't have anyway,' Adam insisted.

'You've got change from the old hag that sits inside the public lav with her begging bowl,' snarled Martin.

'At two in the morning?' said O. 'Has she got change for a large note? A hundred francs, say?'

' — On insertion of the second coin,' babbled Martin, rather red in the face, 'and on dialling the Tel-Hotel digits for the hotel of your choice, you are put in touch with that hotel by Tel-Hotel Tel-Speak, through which you communicate your requirements, these being duly recorded by the Tel-Hotel robot receptionist at the other end.'

'And when you get there,' asked O, 'are you led up to bed by the robot? Will it do tricks with you on request? And do its immoral earnings go to *it* or to Tel-Hotel?'

'No!' bawled Martin. 'When the robot receptionist receives the message, it alerts the human hotel receptionist at the hotel desk — '

' — Why can't you speak direct to this human receptionist in the first place?' Adam said.

' — And the robot receptionist prepares everything for your arrival,' blurted Martin. 'Tel-Hotel makes a profit from the coins inserted in the machine and the ten per cent commission which the hotel pays on the booking.'

'I still don't understand,' I said, 'why you have to speak to the robot receptionist and not direct to the human receptionist.'

'In case the latter is on his security rounds,' said Martin.

'It would have to be a pretty dreadful hotel,' said O, 'if the receptionist doubled as security guard.'

'The smaller hotels,' Martin said, 'often employ a night porter to receive late arrivals *and* to act as a waiter and security guard. So if anyone has rung down for a drink, and the night porter is upstairs screwing whoever ordered it, your booking nevertheless gets through – thanks to Tel-Hotel.'

'If you're going to deal with that sort of hotel,' I said, 'you'll never get your ten per cent.'

'And that kind of place wouldn't pay the rent for the robot,' said O. 'Or are you supplying them free? If you are, your capital outlay — '

' — Now then,' yodelled Martin, 'follow me.' He led us to the ambo and mounted to the higher level. 'I am in a position to arrange the sale, at a special rate, of shares in Tel-Hotel. NOW. This special offer extends only until New Year's Eve. Cheques accepted. Minimum investment – two hundred and fifty pounds.'

'I could give you a cheque,' said O. 'I shall sign it "Minnie Mouse".'

'I very much like the *modern* ring to all this,' said Hamilton Glott: 'it is new, technological, vital. It is of our time. It meets a widely felt nee — '

' — Stop being a cunt,' said Hamish. 'You're going to need everything we've got for buying our house in Corfu.'

'I shan't even consider that,' said Hamilton, 'unless I am allowed to invest some of *my* money in Tel-Hotel. I'm in for five hundred pounds,' he called up to Martin.

'Then you can match it with five hundred for me too,' snarled Hamish at Hamilton. 'If it's free,' he said in an aside to O, 'it can't be bad.'

'Cheque when we get back to the hotel?' said Martin to Hamilton. 'One thousand quid?'

'Two monkeys,' glossed Adam, who even so young was much given to racing parlance.

'I haven't brought my chequebook to Venice,' Hamilton said.

'I have,' said O. 'You can alter the form to fit your own account.'

This would be very unpopular with banks these days but was perfectly acceptable then: most proper hotels, shops and restaurants kept blank cheque forms for the use of their clients.

'I'll think about it,' said Hamilton. 'I am rather reluctant to draw a four-figure cheque on somebody else's chequebook.'

'For Christ's sake stiffen up, you silly little Jew,' said Hamish: 'if you *will* show off, then pay up like a man.'

Hamilton looked as if he were about to cry. This was his habitual response when anyone made an anti-semitic remark to him, though he himself was happy enough to make anti-semitic remarks about other Jews, particularly his father and his stepmother.

We all moved on to the steps behind the altar, jumped the stinking puddle at the bottom of them, and came up the other side to examine, from the best viewpoint, the Mosaic of The Weeping Madonna.

'What a huge tear,' said Adam: 'why only one?'

'She is weeping for the human race,' said O, 'one tear is all it's worth.'

'All right,' said Hamilton to Martin; 'if you'll pay for lunch at the Gritti, I'll give you a cheque for a thousand when we get back to our hotel.'

'Five hundreds' worth of shares for me,' said Hamish, 'and five hundreds' worth for her. I shall look forward to receiving the scrip.'

Martin gave the Madonna a funny look and said nothing.

'When will the scrip arrive?' persisted Hamish.

'After the normal period,' said Martin. 'Please remember that the project is in its infancy.'

Hamilton started skipping, like a squat and ill-conditioned teeny-bopper, on a mosaic floor, which was roped off and surrounded by polite notices of prohibition.

'Oh God,' said Hamish, 'will she never stop making an exhibition of herself? She thinks she's special, you see. No regulations apply to *her*. She deliberately goes to the Ritz without wearing a tie and starts shouting at the head waiter when he won't let her in.'

'Any more of that,' fluted the capering Hamilton, 'and I shan't buy any of Martin's lovely shares for you, *and* I shan't buy this house in Corfu. In fact, I don't really think it's worth going on with that at all. The house is only a shell, it'll cost God knows how much to rebuild it – and anyhow I've bought tickets for the ballet at the Fenice on the 30th of December. After that it'll be time to go back to London. I have got a business to run even if you haven't.'

'Bravo,' I said. 'Perhaps you and your agency will make a bumper New Year effort to get just *some* of my books properly advertised. That's what Anthony Blond employs you for.'

'You'll be lucky,' said Hamish. 'She hasn't paid her printer's bill for ten months. Neither has Blond, come to that.'

Martin stood us luncheon at the Gritti: O lent Hamilton a cheque form: Hamilton wrote out a cheque and 'forgot' to alter the name of the bank and the branch, then climbed on to his bed and started snoring: Hamish inspected the cheque, made the necessary alterations, forged Hamilton's initials, and passed the thing on to Martin before Hamilton woke up, clamorous to go to the winter casino in the Palazzo Calerghi-Vendramin.

Here the gaming rooms are on the second floor, a set of elegant and inter-connecting apartments, suitably decorated in later seventeenth-century style. Since 1980 the gamblers have been accommodated on the first floor, where there are no carpets or decorations, because these days many lorry drivers and other assorted banausics have appeared on the scene who tend, when losing, to fling their lighted cigarettes on the floor or crush them out on any picture or other available fitting. Back in 1969, however, the clientele was still passably good-humoured and on the particular evening of which I write, our party was playing roulette in a long and pleasantly furnished chamber, presided over by a shifty and ill-shaven Loredan at one end and a simpering pair of Grimani (male and female) at the other. There were four tables, to one of which went Hamilton, to another Hamish, and to a third O and myself. Adam, too young to be admitted, had been left behind with Martin who hated gambling, of this kind, and had kindly promised to dine Adam and educate him about politics and the world.

'That Pasha Stevens,' said O, 'he'll keep his hands to himself?'

'Oh, yes. He's to be a parliamentary candidate at the next election. He can't risk a row.'

'If you ask me, potential parliamentary candidates ought not to be getting up things like Tel-Hotel.'

'Everyone is crooked about money these days' – not quite so crooked then as now – 'why not an aspirant MP? Anyway, he'll cover himself very carefully and have at least four secret exits to the backstairs.'

'Hmmm,' snorted O, and looked as if he were about to make ethical pronouncements, but at that moment twenty-seven, *rouge, impair, passe*, came up. Twenty-seven was O's favourite number. Success went to his head, prompting new bets which seemed to comprehend the entire cloth, and he had no leisure to complain further of the Pasha's commercial endeavours.

At the next table, Hamilton, having already borrowed fifty thousand lire from me and the same sum from O, was at last enjoying a winning run, of which O and I were made aware by his screeching and cavorting.

'Goody gumdrops,' he squealed as fourteen came up for the third time running.

Hamilton often exulted in this kind of nursery camp when things were going well for him; when they weren't, he favoured biblical invective or, more commonly, self-pity. 'It's in her Jew blood,' Hamish used to say: 'when we went to Jerusalem a few years back she did a howling and gnashing production at the Wailing Wall.'

O, having lost touch with twenty-seven, joined me at Hamilton's elbow.

'We'd better claim our money back,' I said to O, 'while his streak lasts.'

'Goody gumdrops,' Hamilton iterated and reiterated as twenty, another of his numbers, followed fourteen. I extracted from his pile a plaque of fifty thousand and another for O. Hamilton went on winning for the next three coups, then started to lose rapidly. O took one arm, I took the other, and we hauled him away from the table, as his little froggy legs kicked in the air, still a clear five hundred pounds to the good, in those days a satisfactory sum.

We sat at a bar, underneath the portrait of an odious della Grazia, to celebrate. Hamilton, who knew how to be generous on occasion, ordered French champagne at thirty pounds a bottle. Hamish came up as the cork popped.

'Good,' he said, 'I could do with a little refreshment. Thirsty work, losing at roulette.'

'Good job I won,' said Hamilton. 'Rather a lot. Between us we must have a profit.'

'I doubt it,' said Hamish coolly. 'You remember that bundle of traveller's cheques you got? As a business allowance in order to beat the currency regulations?'

'Seven hundred and fifty pounds?'

'That's right. You let me sign them and keep them in case you lost them . . . or got carried away by lust or vanity, and bought one of the local specialities, either in flesh or glass? Or started flashing the cheques about or giving them to a good cause in order to feel big? Did you ever hear,' he said to O and me, 'how she became one of the

23

sponsors of *Private Eye* when it started? Promised to pay up to five thousand if the mag got into trouble about libel, and then rang up all the columnists to let them know? So open-handed, you see. Of course, in that case she hadn't actually lodged the money, only guaranteed it at need, so the minute the first spot of bother came along and the *Eye* asked for a hundred and fifty pounds, she was thundering on her lawyer's door, whining at him to find ways out.'

'And did he?' said O.

'Oh yes. They got up some story together about how Hamilton was covering only the advertising section of the *Eye*, she being a publicity girl, and so — '

' — How much did you lose?' said Hamilton to Hamish, waving his bouffant hairdo about like the blackamoor in a Punch and Judy show.

'Only seven hundred,' said Hamish. 'I left the last cheque for buying presies for the servants. You'll have to arrange money for this hotel. It's quite easy. Just order it from the firm for "Business Expenses" like the last lot – they can cable it within twenty-four hours. And while you're about it, you'd better tell them to send some to Corfu as well to — '

'Corfu is off,' decreed Hamilton. 'It was never really on, and after this piece of gross irresponsibility — '

'Never use clichés,' said Hamish: 'clichés betray panic. Now then. You're quite sure – that Corfu is off, I mean?'

'Quite.'

'Oh dear. We shall have to send a telegram to Henry Thurso. He's expecting us to dine the day after we arrive – on the twenty-ninth. Remind me to wire him in the morning.'

'Henry Thurso . . . is expecting us to dine on the 29th? In his new house in Corfu?'

'That's what I said. Penrith will probably be there, and that sister of his who married one of the Shah's nephews and managed to win a divorce settlement of half a million . . . after giving him clap and swearing that it was him that first gave it to her.'

'Oh,' said Hamilton Glott. 'It would be a pity to miss seeing Henry Thurso's new house. It's in all the architectural journals.'

'A great pity,' said Hamish. 'Shall I wire or will you?'

'I'll just . . . think it over.'

*

'Of course,' said Hamish, while Hamilton was paying the hotel bill before they left for the airport and Flight OA 247 for Athens/Corfu, 'Henry 19th Earl of Thurso wouldn't put up with *her* in his house for a million quid and advancement to a dukedom. Anyway, he went back to England yesterday.'

'That will make it easier for you,' said Adam: 'you can tell Mr Glott that Lord Thurso was called home suddenly.'

'You're catching on fast, sweetheart. Unlike your old dad, who's still got a lot to learn.'

'What have I got to learn?' I said.

Hamilton appeared, glowing with snobbish expectation. O, Adam and I waved them away on their speedboat to the airport. The desk porter came out on to the boat platform, joined in the waving, and then flapped something under my nose.

'Six tickets for the ballet at the Fenice on the 30th, signore. Signor Glott said that you would know of two more friends to ask, now that he and Signor M'cSass have gone.'

'How kind of Signor Glott,' I said.

'He forgot to pay for them before leaving,' said the desk porter. 'Forty thousand lire each. A total of two hundred and forty thousand.'

'Then I don't think I want them. I loathe the ballet anyhow.'

'We had Signor Glott's assurance in the matter. I fear that the sum has been deducted from the deposit you made on arrival.'

'You'd better surrender,' said O.

'As Mr M'cSass said, Pa, you've still got a lot to learn,' Adam contributed.

'Perhaps Martin will help,' I said. 'He's supposed to like ballet. Where is Martin? I'd have thought he'd be here to see them off.'

'Sorry, chums,' said Martin, bustling up behind us with two bulging briefcases. 'My boat here?' to the porter. 'For the airport?'

'Why didn't you go with Hamish and Hamilton?' O enquired.

'I'm on a later plane – for London. Besides, I don't want Hamilton to know that I'm leaving earlier than advertised. I want that cheque of his in my bank before close of business today, and I'm going to get special

25

clearance. Hamish warned me last night that Hamilton was thinking of cancelling it to make up for the extra money he had to send for.'

'So you don't want him to see you at the airport in case he guesses what you're up to and telephones to cancel the cheque straightaway?' said Adam methodically.

'You're catching on fast, poppet,' said Martin. 'I need all the cash I can raise for the election I've got to fight in Fulham. Not long now.'

'But suppose their plane hasn't left when you arrive?' said Adam. 'There are always delays these days. They'll spot you then all right.'

'After all,' said O, surveying the Pasha's paunch, 'you are a distinguished figure.'

'Hamilton and Hamish will be preening themselves in the VIP Lounge,' Martin said. 'Hamilton paid the manager of the hotel to arrange it. Hamish told me when he was drunk. Me, I'm much too modest for that kind of thing. My constituents, even though they're Conservative – indeed because they're conservative – like me to show the common touch and do like ordinary folk. Chin, chin, chums,' cried Martin as his boat drew up to the landing stage: ' "Wish me luck as you wave me goodbye," ' he sang; ' "Cheerio, here I go, on my way." '

And on his way he went.

'Amusing fellow, that Pasha,' said O. 'I hope he gets in for Fulham. Did I misunderstand him, or is he going to use Hamilton's investment in Tel-Hotel to help fight his election?'

'He told me at dinner,' Adam said, 'the other night when you were all at the casino, that if he becomes a Member of Parliament he will have command of "virtually unlimited credit". So of course it won't matter then – he'll be able to settle with everybody. It's called Flexible Funding, he told me. You get money to finance one thing and use it for another; then you get money for something else, at least if you're a politician you do, and use that to replace the original lot – but only if it's urgent, of course. All governments do it, he said, and so do all big business firms. They never pay cash, Mr Stevens said, if they can get credit, because they may be able to jew their way out of paying at all.'

'Did Mr Stevens use the word "jew"?' said O.

'Yes. I don't think he likes Jews very much. In fact, he told me he didn't. But he has a lot of Jewish friends, he said, because he enjoys trying to jew them back, if you see what I mean. Although they're such

26

frightful screws, he said, they're very conceited and that makes it quite easy to jew them. He has one friend called Benjamin Crud, who thinks he knows everything in the world about Art. So Mr Stevens got one of his friends in Chelsea to hack a bit of concrete about in a Tate Gallery sort of way and then showed the thing to Mr Crud and said it was an early Salvador Dali – one of the few sculptures he ever did – of Lot's wife masturbating. That was why she looked back on Sodom, you see. It gave her a huge thrill and she started playing with herself, and now here was Dali's carving of her just about to "bring herself off", as Mr Stevens put it. Well, in the first place Mr Crud was very excited by the subject – "Old queens get very frottish about lesbian goings on", Mr Stevens told me —; and in the second place Mr Stevens had got another artistic friend to write a paragraph in one of the colour supplements about Dali's "very rare and early sculptures, one of the finest of which is reputed to be the lost work in concrete of Lot's wife engaged in self-abuse while looking back on the cities of the plain". The paragraph went on to describe what this looked like, and of course it looked exactly like the bit of rubbish which Mr Stevens was showing Mr Crud . . . who paid him twenty-five thousand pounds for it, thinking it was really worth twice as much – which it was according to the man who did the write-up. *He* was quite a famous art critic, Mr Stevens said, but he very badly needed ten thousand pounds, so he consented to join in the joke. So everyone was happy – the chap who hacked the concrete was fobbed off with £20. He couldn't read, you see, so he didn't know what was happening. And the critic got his ten thousand, and Mr Stevens got all the rest.'

'I know Benj Crud a bit,' I said. 'Perhaps I can get something out of Martin by threatening to split.'

'You're beginning to catch on, Pa,' said Adam, 'but I'm afraid you're too late. After a while Mr Crud found out that he'd been done, but of course he couldn't do anything about it, Mr Stevens told me, because if he did everyone would have known that he was just a trendy old yid who didn't know anything about Art after all. His vanity, Mr Stevens said, was even greater than his avarice.'

'Did the Pasha use the word "yid"?' O asked. 'Because if he did that's two words of racial abuse he used: "yid" and "Jew".'

'Jew is just a description,' I said, 'not a word of abuse.'

27

'The Pasha used "jew" as a *verb*,' said O. 'He said that governments and business firms "jew their way out of" this or that.'

'Perfectly sound English.'

'No,' said O. 'There was a court case. Someone applied for an injunction against the word "jew" being listed as an adjective or a verb in a new dictionary that was being got up. "He is a Jew," is quite all right, but "he is my jew taylor, and he's jewed me over the bill" is not all right – or so the man who asked for the injunction claimed. The judge, who was a yid himself, granted the injunction. So the pasha would not be popular, in certain quarters, for the language he used to Adam.'

'I shan't squawk,' Adam said.

'There are others as would,' said O, 'political enemies or rivals. I think that the Pasha *is* rather indiscreet. I like him the more for it, but I predict a sad end for him.'

(A very sound prediction, as it turned out, but not quite in the sense intended by O.)

'All of this is getting us no further,' I said, 'with my little problem of the two hundred and forty thousand lire that I've been *jewed* out of by bloody Glott. The charge for those accursed tickets has used most of the deposit with which I intended to pay the hotel bill.'

'Never pay cash,' said Adam, 'if you can get credit. I know you've got credit cards, Papa.'

'I'm not allowed to use them abroad without special permission. And then only for about twopence.'

So the law said on the morning of 28th December (my birthday) 1969. But I'd reckoned without my birthday present. Mr Roy Jenkins, of blessed memory for this if for very little else, announced later that day that with immediate effect as from New Year's Day, 1970, Englishmen abroad could make full use of credit cards and could cash cheques on their English banks if they had cheque cards to support them.

O, Adam and I celebrated with gusto at Harry's. O even forgot himself to the extent of cashing a minute cheque, with the proceeds of which he bought a glass frog resembling Hamilton Glott, from a swish glassworks on the Grand Canal. Since the management had sent a special boat to our hotel to collect O, a service procured for him by the desk porter with whom he seemed to be rather a favourite, the reception committee which showed him round was rather unhappy about O's

28

stingy purchase and did not offer him a free ride back. He was in fact trapped in the rain on the firm's landing stage, the door having been firmly locked on him the minute he'd got outside, for an hour and a half.

'That's what comes of being mean,' Adam said.

'You must understand,' said O, 'that I am in fact half-Jewish, on my mother's side. She's a real cow.'

'I know,' I said, having met her. 'But if she's also a Jewess that makes you, in kosher law, a real pukka Jew, not just half.'

'Fair enough,' said O: 'and I am delighted to recall how massively I jewed those glass people. That expensive ride in a speed boat – and all I bought was one hundred lire's worth of glass frog.'

Which stands to this day on his mantel next to a photo of Hamilton Glott puffing up his ego over lunch at the Gritti; it recalls that fable of Aesop's about the frog that tried to blow itself up into a bull, and bears witness if I lie.

PART TWO

East Of Suez

i)   *Flower of the rose*

Flower o' the rose,
If I've been merry, what matter who knows?

Robert Browning *Fra Lippo Lippi: 11. 68/69*

In the autumn of 1946, when I first came to India as a cadet destined for the OTS at Bangalore, I was desperately afraid lest I had caught the pox.

Soon after a brief encounter with a jolly whore from Piccadilly while on embarkation leave, I had found a small pustule at the base of my penis. It was, of course, only a casual pimple, but guilt promoted it to the menacing status of a primary chancre and it was some time before a kindly Eurasian medical officer, consulted on impulse while he was engaged in checking my fitness for a boxing tournament, set my mind at rest. For several weeks before this I had been rather heavily punished for my caprice of venal venery by a nagging fear of waking up one morning covered from head to foot with secondary syphilitic ulcers. The lesson, however, was as salutary as it was severe: ever afterward I remained, not indeed chaste, but scrupulously attentive to hygienic precaution, to my great mental and physical benefit.

And there was to be another and very different kind of benefit from my fear of infection, a bonus which accrued shortly after the dusky captain of the RIAMC had assured me that all was well. It so happened that a Danish cadet – in 1946 many such were still being trained by the British – being next in the queue for examination by the MO, had heard my exchange with him and spread the tale about. 'There was Raven,' this Dansker told his cronies, 'having his heart listened to, when suddenly he drops his knickers and flops his lot on the table in front of this chee-chee medic and says "Get a look at this".' The story went the rounds and one evening a large and luscious blond from the Danish platoon shuffled into my basha (bedroom), and said he wanted to consult me confidentially.

What actually had I had on my prick, he asked, that had been urgent enough to consult the MO, but had then been dismissed by him as harmless? He himself had – well – a 'spot' that worried him: if it turned out to be similar to mine, clearly he need worry no more. Let us, then, compare notes – or better still, for the sake of absolute clarity, let us compare our parts. This we did. The comparison dispelled anxiety in him and aroused desire in both of us; relief and gratitude made for tenderness, youth for fervour, and Eros came to a fine and generous conclusion, brimming and flooding beneath my mosquito net.

Remorse, his, followed ecstasy. He burst out from under the net before I had time to counsel the stillness which overcomes disgust, guiltily huddled into his uniform, ran from my basha, slamming the door. In twenty minutes, however, he was back, insisting on one more comparison of *pudenda* 'to make quite certain'.

'The trouble with a lot of these cadets,' said Sydney Bryanstone, a contemporary at Charterhouse and now some months senior to me in the OTS, 'is that a lot of them, English as well as Danish, didn't have the blessings of a public school education. Those sort of chaps get very crabby, at first, after being seduced. Quite apart from growing up in day schools, the Danes in particular are much battered in their youth by the fiercer kind of Protestant pronouncement.'

Both of us sucked hard on our whisky.

'In general,' Sydney continued, 'mosquito nets are a great help in promoting frolics; people think that God can't see through them because a mosquito net is pretty well part of the bedclothes. All children when playing with themselves, assume that neither God nor Mummy can see through the bedclothes. It is a beneficent psychological dispensation. It facilitates seduction, but does not do away with the aftermath of guilt as those seduced, even public school boys, often think they have betrayed their manhood. The stupidity of human beings is limitless. For myself,' said Sydney Bryanstone, 'I don't care all that much for homosexual practice, but it has its points, as the classical authors have made plain to us, and it is certainly a godsend at this OTS.'

'Amen.'

'Not only that. It's been a great help to me in my Army career.'

'Ohhh?' I said.

'My platoon commander,' said spindle-shanked, spotty Sydney Bryanstone, 'is in love with me. Don't be surprised. I know I'm about as attractive as a broken umbrella, but there's something about me, there always has been, something emanating from me, which fills anyone, male or female, inside a range of four foot or so, with a kind of sexual frenzy. It's often a great bore, but in the case of Captain Ram Patel it has been very useful. Any other commander would have sent me back to a junior company or even back into the ranks by now, I'm so bloody useless; but Patel has positively promised to pass me out with the rest of the platoon in three weeks' time.'

'Do you sleep with him?'

'Good God, no. I wouldn't sleep with a wog. But we do it in the jungle during exercises – times like that. My other conquest is white, thank goodness: Captain Gregory Farr, the cricket officer. When I got off with him, I thought I'd do myself a bit of good by saying I'd been in the XI at school. Quite apart from anything else, if you get into the OTS Cricket XI, you are excused a great deal of tedious training, for net prackker and so on. So I announced I was a Colour at Charterhouse, got into the XI here on the strength of it — '

' — But you were only in the Third XI at school.'

'I know, I know, and it very soon became apparent. But by that time Gregory Farr had fallen for my circumambient sex appeal, and he put down all my goofing to "a run of bad luck". It's been going on for five months now, that run of bad luck, so it should keep me in the team – and incidentally get me off three days of our final bush manoeuvre – for the few matches that are left before I pass out.'

'Do you sleep with Captain Farr?'

'No. We do it in the pavilion lav. He thinks that if you do it standing up you aren't really queer, just making the best of what's going. Anyhow, he comes the moment I touch him, so it's not too much of a chore. He doesn't even want me to come too. Now then: what about a little turn, you and I?'

'I don't really — '

' — Let me get within four foot of you. Try out the old effluent . . .'

'. . . Yes. Yes, Sydney. I see what you mean . . .'

The Bangalore of the middle Forties was a cosy little cantonment town, full of pleasant Indian and Chinese restaurants, cinemas showing English and American films, and eccentric hotels staffed by loyal Indian servants and run by Army widows. There were parks where yelping brown children played cricket; tiny squares in which cross-legged tailors put together Service Dress jackets of inferior cut, and material, for newly commissioned cadets, also of inferior cut and material. There were long, wide avenues lined with antique cannon and venerable box trees. Along these the tongas rattled gaily, hand-drawn rickshaws ground their way behind rasping, emaciated rickshaw wallahs, who squirted blood and betel, and on the verges middle-class Indian clerks and students went decorously hand in hand.

'I do hate the way they hold hands as they walk,' said James Prior, as we proceeded in a tonga to the evening performance of *The Picture of Dorian Gray*, starring George Saunders as the honey-voiced Lord Henry and some American called Crawford in a womanising misrepresentation of the antihero. 'They look so sloppy. And I wish they wouldn't wear their shirts outside their skirt arrangements.'

'Their dhotis. It really isn't any of our business,' I said. 'After all it is, by right, their country. And very soon now they're going to get it back.'

'Do they want it back?' said James.

'The professional middle classes, certainly. So that they can shout the odds and the orders. You can see how the King's Indian commissioned officers are beginning to enjoy themselves. Like Ram Patel,' I said, thinking of Sydney Bryanstone. 'I don't think the princes will like Independence, and I don't suppose the peasants care much either way. But like it or not, they've got it coming – and now Lord Louis Mountbatten's here to organise the takeover a year earlier than originally planned.'

'Bad news, Lord Louis. Conceited, socialist, dictatorial. Stupid idea, bring forward Independence. The Hindu-Muslim shindigs are going to be ghastly. If only it could all be left another year as previously arranged, we might be able to set things up more tidily.'

'The Americans want us to hand over immediately.'

'Has no one told them,' said James, 'about the inevitable blood-letting?'

'Americans don't listen. They're even more conceited than Lord Louis. Besides, Roosevelt is senile.'

'Surely,' said James, 'Roosevelt is dead.'

'Is he? I don't bother much with what goes on in America. Nasty smells and noises: keep out.'

'Then how do you know they want us to leave India prematurely?'

'It's just the sort of thing they would want. They're jealous of our Empire.'

I record this near-imbecile conversation because it was typical of the time and did contain just a grain of truth. Indian Independence *was* prematurely declared: there has recently been a book by a very senior Indian officer condemning the folly and wickedness of advancing the date, and thereby causing a nationwide shambles. I would also agree, now as then, with what James said of Mountbatten: not only conceited but also false, as many of his general officers and others had already discovered. But all that is by the way.

After the film (how poor Oscar would have squirmed), James and I went to the pavilion of the OTS cricket ground for some supper; it doubled as an Officers' and O/Cadets' Club. Captain Gregory Farr was there, making sure, as officer i/c cricket, that a proper luncheon had been arranged for the OTS match versus the Combined Gunners & Sappers the next day. Both James and I would be playing, and thus avoiding an annoying route march. 'Fighting fit for the morrow –whaaat?' said Farr. 'Pity we shan't have Sydney Bryanstone' – who was by this time away in the hills on his commissioning leave – 'always a tower of strength. Mind you, he's had wretched luck since he's been here, when one thinks of what he might have done. I gather his average for your First XI at Charterhouse during his last season was well over forty.'

'First XI?' said James, who had not heard about Sydney's romancing in this area. 'I believe he once made twenty-three not out for the Third.'

'Some mistake,' said Farr, going red.

Curried eggs arrived for James and me. Farr stood over us. 'Some mistake,' he repeated.

'Possibly,' said James. 'It may only have been twenty-one not out, or it may have been in a house match, but whatever it was it wasn't for the First XI.'

'But Sydney told me himself — '

' — Never mind, sir,' I said, seeking peace. 'Memories are very short over this kind of thing.' I kicked James' shin under the table. 'I was once accused of making a duck against Eton, whereas in fact — '

' — Never mind about your fluky innings against Eton,' said James, infuriated by my kick, 'Sydney Bryanstone never played for the Charterhouse XI. And there were those that said that you should not have done either, that if you hadn't sucked up to the master in charge of cri — '

' — What a very nasty mood you're in, Prior,' said Gregory Farr, but suddenly too preoccupied (why?) to take in properly what was being said either about me or Sydney: 'I hope you're more agreeable tomorrow.'

Turning to look after the retreating Gregory, I realised we had been saved by the bell, or rather the beau. Sydney's successor in the rôle of Gregory Farr's *deliciae* had just appeared, and the inflamed cricket officer, forgetting all else, no longer mindful of king, country, or commission, let alone of revelations about Sydney Bryanstone's concoctions, was thrusting in top gear for the pavilion bogatry.

'It's too bad of Bryanstone to tell such lies about his cricket,' said James. 'Why did you stand up for him?'

'I like Sydney. I don't want him to get into trouble.'

'He should have his commission taken away. Charterhouse First XI indeed!'

'Don't be such a prig. As if it matters to anybody. And thank you for saying such charming things about my place in the First.'

'Sorry,' said James, reverting swiftly, as he always did, to equanimity. 'But it was a bit much. That kick — '

' — Right,' I said. 'Apologies from me, too, and now let's forget the whole thing. But don't contradict Captain Farr again on the topic, because it's one he finds particularly sensitive, and we don't want him to get cross with us and chuck us out of the side – when we get off so many bloody beastly chores by being in it.'

'Ah,' said James, his old-fashioned conscience beginning to heave, 'that's another thing that worries me. I'm not sure we ought to avoid so much important training just to play cricket.'

Tiresome as this line of country was, at least it led him away from the perilous subject of Sydney Bryanstone before he did his sums and deduced that Farr's fatuity could only arise from infatuation, a discovery which would have bothered him very much indeed and might even have caused him to make an official complaint and thus caused scandal injurious to many people's pleasure and comfort.

As the days passed, Independence for India drew nearer and nearer; but in the enclave of Bangalore life went on as though the Raj would never end. The trumpets and bugles sounded the old calls; the columns, both Indian and English, obeyed the old orders and marched to the old tunes. Every month there was a race meeting which began with a polo scurry and ended with God Save the King; most days there was cricket on the grass wicket of the OTS ground, the most beautiful in Southern India if not the entire subcontinent, while the regimental bands, both British and Indian, uttered medleys from *Lilac Time* and *Rose Marie*; most days, also, there were tennis parties at the larger houses and at the dotty hotels. At such a party I encountered Second Lieutenant Sydney Bryanstone, recently returned from his furlough in the Nilgri Hills. His sweaty white flannels clung to his jejune thighs and soggily delineated his skeletal crutch: after many weeks deprived of sexual entertainment, for my big blond had had some kind of accident in training and had been ferried away by the boatman, I lusted for Sydney, double-yolker zits and all.

I drew him urgently aside to engage him to dine that evening at the Officers' and O/Cadets' Club. He accepted with a seigneurial nod. Later, back in my basha, I made my avid advance.

'Too late, Simon,' said Sydney. 'I grant you we had a lot of fun while I was still a cadet; but this sort of thing is beneath the dignity of an officer. Once a fellow is commissioned, the girls take an interest.'

'Such as they are here,' I said. 'Randy memsahibs, if you're lucky. Otherwise the daughters and female hangers-on, hungry for marriage.'

'I concede that the white women in India are a pretty horrible crew. But officers really can't go feeling up other chaps like fourth-form tarts back at school.'

'Why not? Your old friend Captain Farr wouldn't agree with you.'

'Gregory Farr will come to a bad end. Listen to me, Simon. As James Prior would tell you, this kind of thing will not do if you have to run an Army. It was all very jolly in the old days, and I'm not passing any moral judgements now: I'm simply saying that if Officers go on fancying other chaps, they will end up fancying the lance corporal on the right of the front rank of their platoon, and then there will be trouble.'

'They can confine themselves to other officers or to cadets.'

'Far too many officers and cadets these days, as you very well know, are oiks. Oiks don't understand this business. They don't understand that when you are asked you either do it or decline the offer politely and keep your mouth shut. Oiks enjoy moral indignation; they enjoy making a row and being the centre of attention. Other-rank oiks can be vengeful; officer oiks are often self-righteous; both kinds have girl-friends or 'fiancies' as they call them, to which, God knows why, they think they ought to be faithful. Even public school boys can sometimes get up a fuss if you goose them, especially the Catholics. Once you're an officer, Simon, the game is no longer worth the candle.'

'All right. I believe you. But one last little flurry before you go off to join your battalion?'

''Fraid not,' said Sydney Bryanstone. 'It's nice to know that you're still falling for my emanations . . . but one really must put away childish things.'

'I think you're bloody mean. I paid for your dinner.'

Rory Parkes came fussing in to borrow a bush-shirt for the morning.

'There you are,' said Sydney, after Rory had gone fussing out again with the borrowed shirt. 'That shirt of yours is going to be four times too big for him. It's quite clear that it was just an excuse, that dear little Rory was prying — '

' — Or just exciting himself.'

'And in either case, had he found us on the job, would have gone off chattering like a Chinee with his mousetrap mouth — '

' — He'd have found us under the mosquito net. If we'd simply kept still he wouldn't have known anything about it. *You* taught me about mosquito nets.'

'I'm sorry, Simon. Mrs Henneker "Honeypot" Crichton-Smith, who owns the hotel where we met this afternoon, will give me a nice soapy hand-job any day of the month, and there'd be no need to worry if Lord Louis himself arrived in the middle of it.'

'He'd probably ask to join in,' I said spitefully, 'at least until he saw your skinny fesses.'

'An interesting matter of conjecture,' said Sydney: 'would my emanations work on Lord Louis despite the unattractive nature of my apparatus? But of course one has given all that up, even with Lord Louis. From what I hear he is not to be trusted. Too good at gliding away and leaving one in the shit, if it suits him. As he did with that unfortunate Major-General — what was his name? – Black Jack Grover.'

'You're not accusing Lord Louis of having done it with Black Jack Grover? And then shopping him?'

'Almost worse,' said Sydney. 'There was a very important battle, in which Black Jack was told to hold his divisional front at any cost. *Any cost*. So he did – at a very heavy cost. "These, in the day when heaven was falling. The hour when earth's foundations fled," etc, etc. Black Jack saved the "sum of things" as Housman had it. Very appropriate, as Black Jack was in the Shropshire Light Infantry, the regiment which Housman wrote about, and had once commanded their First Battalion – the 53rd of Foot. So Black Jack Grover saved Lord Louis' bacon and possibly the whole of the Indian Empire as well. And what was his reward? You lost too many men, said Lord Louis. You said no limit, answered Black Jack. I don't want any of your lip, said Lord Louis: back to London with you, and of my bounty I will find you a manky staff desk for the rest of the war – providing you never again step one single centimetre out of line. So you do understand, Simon, why I shouldn't be doing it with Lord Louis, even if I hadn't given it up. He's the sort of chap that would cut off your private parts and keep them as a souvenir.'

After we were commissioned in May of 1947 – about two months after Sydney had finally departed from Bangalore and become a highly successful regimental officer – James, Rory Parkes and I, among others, went to the same hill station that Sydney had patronised for a fortnight's leave. The Raj was still banging along there all right: in hill stations it never really stopped. There was golf, racing, hunting, tennis and croquet. Mrs Gertie Spofforth-Spalding, the sporty old brigadier-general's relict who ran our pension, fiercely fancied first James, who told her untruthfully that he was engaged to be married, then little gold Rory, who was terrified of her early manual manoeuvres but at length allowed himself to be hoisted between her huge hunkers . . . after which he became quite vain of his attractions and put on worldly airs.

James, who could not bear vanity in any form, began to tease him. While he took a bleak view of homosexual goings-on (for pretty much the same reasons as Sydney Bryanstone now did), James found heterosexual activity, except in marriage, somewhat comic.

'What does she *say*, Rory?' said James as we played a three-ball on the mountain golf course.

'She says it's never been quite like this before,' said Rory stoutly.

'I don't suppose it has. It's not every old women is lucky enough to have and to hold someone young enough to be her grandson. Does she keep a special dimple in her knee for you? What do *you* say at moments of passion? What do you call her?'

A long pause. Rory then missed an important putt of less than a yard. Although he was undoubtedly shy in such matters and probably resented enquiry, he clearly had something he wished to divulge to us and was agitated lest he be mocked or disbelieved.

'I have to call her Sibylla,' Rory said at last. 'I have to say, "Sibylla, what do you wish?" Apparently that's what the children said to the Sibyl at Cumae, when she was hanging up in a jar, and the Sibyl always answered, "ἀποθανεῖν θέλω-" – "I wish to die." But my Sibylla answers me, "I wish to die the little death." And then she does. And so do I. It goes back to something she learnt from a lover a long time ago. When her husband was down in the plains . . . and she was up here with all the other women because the plains were considered too hot for them. That often happened, she has told me, and lots of the women took lovers, though it was never mentioned.'

'Kipling mentioned it,' I said.

'Kipling was a cad,' said James. 'He was always saying things that broke the rules.'

'Sibylla's lover is buried in the cemetery here,' said Rory.

'She's made it all up,' I said.

'Perhaps,' said Rory. 'But I've seen his grave. He was called Cornet Jeremy Joyce-Hicks. He died of some tropical illness at the age of twenty-two. That's why he was up here. He thought he was convalescing but really he was dying. He liked to make love to Sibylla as often as possible because this helped him to believe that he was getting stronger. Sibylla used all . . . all her talents to make him potent, because this, she says, gave him hope and happiness, though in fact it was helping to kill him. But that didn't matter, she says, as he was bound to die pretty soon in any case. So they went on making love till just a very few days before his death. In 1905 . . . when he was twenty-two,' Rory repeated: 'that's what it says on his grave.'

'She could be having a fantasy,' James remarked, in an ordinary voice but a kind one. 'She could have been walking through the graveyard, and seen his grave, and thought, "How sad", and imagined Cornet Jeremy Joyce-Hicks as a fantasy lover. A lot of people do that kind of thing, you know.'

'Sometimes,' Rory said, 'I imagine it is 1905 again, and I am Jeremy Joyce-Hicks. I imagine Sibylla as she might have been then . . . and what it must have been like to make love to her. I look rather like Jeremy did, she says.'

'Then why,' I said (God, how objectionable I was), 'did she try James first? You and James are totally different. As he says, the whole thing is an old woman's fantasy.'

'When we do that bit about "Sibylla, what do you wish?" ' said Rory, 'she looks, she really looks, about twenty. Soft and glowing.'

'You imagine it, as you said yourself. Anyway, how do you know? Do you keep the light on?'

'Yes,' said Rory stubbornly. 'She likes to see me, she says. When we get on to the bed, she looks like she always looks. Then we do things which she has taught me, and while we do them she gets younger and younger, until she looks almost like a little girl. That's when she says, "I wish to die the little death." After we have, she begins, but quite slowly, to get old again. When I go away to my room, she looks just as she does now.'

We sat down on a bench by the next tee, waiting for the four-ball in front to go clear. James took out a card. 'Simon, two points,' he said, 'James, four points; Rory, none. Are you sure, Rory, about Mrs Gertie Spofforth-Spalding . . . getting young?'

'He imagines it,' I repeated.

'No,' said Rory. 'I start by imagining it, as I told you, but then she really does. All of her does. Her legs become smooth; her breasts small and firm, instead of like jellyfish; her nipples point; the hair on her tummy feels silky instead of spiky. I do not understand it. But it is true. We shall not speak of this again.'

'We' didn't speak of it again, but James and I did.

We were all back in Bangalore; our last night; the next morning we were to take train for Bombay. Rory was dining with our company commander, whose wife was a distant cousin; James and I were in the Officers' and O/Cadets' Club in the cricket pavilion, eating curried eggs.

'Mrs Spofforth-thing,' I said, 'perhaps in Rory's embrace she was transformed by love. Or perhaps,' I sneered, 'it was something to do with the mysterious East.'

'Mrs Spofforth-Spalding,' said James. 'Do her the courtesy to say her name right. My view is that Rory was unsighted by his first intense sexual encounters. Mrs Spofforth-Spalding was transformed, yes, but only in the eye of her beholding lover.'

'Lover?'

'Let us give him the benefit of the doubt. He spoke very tenderly of her.'

'Yes. Perhaps he has the soul and vision of a poet.'

'I doubt it,' said James. 'He is a very literal sort of person: full of common sense, concerned with practical detail.'

'But can we really accept . . . that Mrs Spofforth-Spalding underwent a true, physical change . . . became at the approach of orgasm . . . her younger self? Almost in her girlhood, Rory said.'

'Rory swears to it and Rory is truthful. He was, I think, anxious that we should know. Perhaps he thought that it was too magical – or too horrible – a secret to bear alone. Now, then. I have known women look twice their age immediately after love,' said James: 'it is a peculiarity of a certain kind of woman, the kind that uses up a lot of energy and enthusiasm in the initial processes before the act itself. Before it can be used, such energy must be summoned and gathered: perhaps that could make a woman look much younger? Before she spent the force and then looked older – quite haggard in one case I remember. I have seen the latter, but never the former. I have seen delight followed by senile fatigue; I have never at any stage seen rejuvenation of the extreme kind reported by Rory.'

'I have known people,' I said, 'who look suddenly much livelier at the *prospect* of sexual action. Their skin develops a glow, a sheen, a patina of pleasure. But all that was in anticipation. And of course they were young anyhow.'

James fielded the bill. 'We'll walk home,' he said, 'settle our digestions.' And a little later, as we started down the murram path under the eucalyptus trees alongside the avenue which led back to the OTS, 'Consider the succubus. It is an evil spirit which puts on the flesh of a desirable woman and comes to monks and holy men to seduce them.'

'A succubus will only come to them in their dreams, surely.'

'I think not. It can put on actual flesh, as I say, and come when its victims are awake. This may be rare, but it happens. Succubi of all kinds and sexes came to Saint Anthony in the desert. Saint Jerome was plagued by them in his own hermitage. He kept a sharp stone which he used to grind into his navel in order to purge his body of lascivious intent.'

A rickshaw passed us illicitly occupied by two cadets instead of the single person permitted by regulation, whether civil or military. Somewhere, far off to the right, towards the Indian bazaar, there was much silly tinkling of tinselly bells. The night was still, allowing a sweet, heavy smell of burning dung to hover along the leaves and branches above us like the Angel of Death, peering, prying, refusing to pass on.

47

'Ghosts have roused desire,' James said: 'they can simulate flesh and blood. Or again, there are those that say that risen corpses can take on, at least briefly, the appetising warmth of living bodies.'

'What have you been reading?'

'Books on the folklore about vampires. There are, rather oddly, several in the OTS library. If a vampire is to come close enough to embrace a human being and suck blood, he or she must first attract. Many of them, like the vampires of the Dolomites and the Abruzzi, do not wish to suck blood, simply to make love in the normal fashion.'

'They must suck blood,' I said, 'in order to keep their bodies – that is, their cadavers – properly nourished.'

'But they will sometimes be well enough nourished to forego blood and simply to fornicate.'

'Are you suggesting,' I said, 'that Mrs Spofforth-thing was some kind of revenant?'

'Mrs Spofforth-*Spalding*. I am simply suggesting that the return of youth and beauty to her body during sexual intercourse may be in some way analogous to the process that enables ghosts to put on physical dimensions, or vampires to entice human lust.'

The avenue turned into the main entrance of the OTS and we continued along a humbler road to the cadet lines, where we were now staying in our former quarters for our few days in transit. The long, low hutments were just visible by the starlight in front of us and to the left: on the right lay the servants' lines, where crude but sound wooden sheds divided into exiguous family apartments sheltered the bearers and the dhobis, the civilian (as distinct from military) syces and Arms-Kote orderlies, the cooks and punkah wallahs and gardeners. The sweepers, refuse-burners and latrine cleaners were Untouchables, if not Unseeables, and lived God knew where, emerging after midnight to do their unspeakable offices and vanishing like the spirits of the damned when the first cock crew. There had just been a wedding or a funeral or some such among the servants, for the drums were rattling tattoos to which all might dance in celebration of fertility or death.

'I once went across the road,' I said, 'to watch their antics.'

'The more fool you. The servants' lines are absolutely out of bounds – on pain of being sent back to the ranks.'

'I knew that, of course. I was drunk, and hoped I might find a woman. Or something.'

'Their women are virtuous,' said James: 'any available woman would have been a whore, almost worse than the ghosts or vampires of which we have been talking, for she would have given you the pox. The worst that can happen to a human being who consorts with the undead is to find that his paramour has reverted prematurely and that he is rutting with a skeleton.'

'Or a corpse,' I said: 'not wholesome.'

'A succubus, who is stable in condition, would certainly be preferable. Though of course to a holy man who has succumbed to temptation a succubus will appear, after coition, as vile as any corpse.'

'But we are surely not suggesting any of these uninviting rôles for Rory's Mrs Spofforth-Spalding.'

'No. But I think she might have been a witch – possibly without knowing it. You remember Roger Sprott at School?'

'Yes. A frightful prig.'

'A bit po-faced, but a decent fellow by and large. Unlike you. Dependable, Roger was,' said James. 'Well, I once met his mother. She was a witch. Not a friendly one, like Mrs Spofforth-Spalding, who turns young and sexy with the right kind of attention: but a sly, sibilant woman, who turned into a hornet-tailed harpy when contradicted or crossed. Roger annoyed her on this occasion, by praising some beak she disliked – little Sniffy Russell, whom she accused of wangling his way out of the war — '

' — But he was well over military age.'

'He looked young, that was why she hated him, and she went round all the parents, when she got half a chance, telling them he was a "pansy". Well, Roger happened to say how beautifully he played the piano and what funny jokes he told. I think he wanted to bait her, because she'd just told him he couldn't come and stay with me in Norfolk. Her face sort of slipped sideways, into a quivering rhombus, and she began to pour out obscenities about poor Sniffy: how he ought to be in prison for dodging the column and perverting young boys. One would have thought she was unstoppable. Then someone she knew came over to the table where we were having lunch and she exercised instantaneous self-control. Her face clicked back into its usual shape and expression, wary but not displeasing, and the words that came out of her mouth flowed calmly and sensibly on about clothes rationing and about how she might just be able to raise enough coupons for Roger to have a new jacket. And by the way, what did her friend think of Mr Russell. . . ?'

'It sounds like a case of old-fashioned tantrum or jealousy to me,' I said, 'rather than witchery.'

'Oh, she was a witch all right,' said James, 'you see, I'd backed up Roger about Sniffy, and when I got back to school I found my best trousers rotten with moth. They'd been perfectly all right when I set out, I guarantee that.'

We turned on to a short path and stepped up on to a verandah. James' basha was some two or three before mine.

'So,' I said: 'the last night in the old home.'

'Yes. I shall miss it – for a few days.'

'They say that India holds on to you for the rest of your life. That you always yearn to come back.'

'Not me,' said James. 'All this dirt. Natives with limbs like stalks. Incessant whinging lies. Red spirts of betel juice. Loathsome smells.'

'And the witches of the Nilgri Hills . . . one of whom has humped our innocent little Rory.'

'So long as she hasn't put a spell on him . . .'

On the train from Bangalore to Bombay we halted somewhere, anywhere, in the yellow plain of the Deccan. Rory gazed over it.

'I miss Gertie Spofforth-Spalding,' he said: 'my Sibylla. She was fun. But you were well out of it, James. She's given me the clap.'

'Lucky it's not the pox,' said James tersely.

'It may be that as well. The Indian civilian doctor I went to in Bangalore says it's too early for a test. You must wait six weeks before you have a Wassermann, he says. It'll be just about time when we get back to England.'

'Try explaining that to Mummy when you ask her to send for a local doctor. "What shall I say is the matter, Rory dear?" "A Wassermann." "A Wassermann, darling? Whatever kind of illness is that?" '

'I shall go to somebody I know in London,' Rory said. 'I've got a godfather who's a doctor. A man of the world. My only worry is that they'll keep us waiting a long time for a ship.'

'They are in no hurry to get us home,' James said.

The trouble was that nobody wanted us at all. The original intention had been to send us, when we were commissioned, to serve with British regiments in India or further East; but now Attlee, under pressure from the populace to keep his election promises, was 'bringing the boys home' and us among them – with the lowest priority of all. We were very young, we were unmarried; why bother with us? True, a lot of money had been spent in training us to be officers; but with the rate of demobilisation dictated by political expediency, there would shortly be nobody for us to command. The only reason why we weren't being left to rot in India for a while was that the Americans were hysterical in their demands for total evacuation of imperialist limeys.

'It's all rather a pity,' said James as we sat in the station restaurant at Poonah, where we had left the train to dine. 'I'm not all that keen on India, but I could have done with a little longer in the East. I shall, after all, be spending the rest of my life in East Anglia.'

'It's a godsend to me, that we're going home,' said Rory. 'I don't trust the native doctors and of course I can't go to an Army one. If I've got syphilis they'll take my commission away.'

'If the wrong people get to know about it,' said James, 'they'll take it away from you just for having clap.'

'I don't know,' I said. 'That half-caste doctor in the Indian Medical Corps was pretty tolerant when I asked him to check my parts back in Bangalore.'

'You hadn't got anything,' said James. 'It's not a matter of morals, it's a matter of appearances. And come to that,' he said to Rory, 'it only takes two or three days to get rid of the clap. Surely that worry at least is out of the way?'

'I can't be sure. I paid a lot of money for injections, but they don't seem to have done much good.'

'So much for those quacks in the bazaar,' said James. 'Qualification: Failed First MB Madrasee. Don't you worry, Rory. By hook or crook we'll find someone reliable in Bombay. We shan't be that far out in the transit camp at Deolali, and the chaps that are running it will be only too pleased to get us out of the way for a day or two.'

'So long as we're not out of the way when the boat sails,' I said.

I was beginning to have the fear, common to all men who have ever been in an Army transit camp, of being accidentally left behind, of being forgotten and ceasing, officially, to exist.

'Don't start getting nervy,' said James. 'I'll sort everything out, with the officer i/c repatriation when we arrive.'

Thank God, I thought for the thousandth time, for James: with James around you need think of nothing for yourself.

A bell sounded. James beckoned. A flurry of waiters appeared at our table to accept his payment of our bill. We sauntered out, while other diners howled for attention, nagged and goaded by memsahibs who clawed the tablecloth in their terror of missing the train.

'Perhaps it is time,' said James, 'that the Indians should have Independence. God only knows what has hypnotised them into accepting the Raj for so long.'

'I expect it was all better before the war,' said Rory, 'before all these jumped-up temporary officers came here.'

'Jumped-up, temporary officers like us,' I said. 'I've no doubt at all you're right, Rory. Things were far better *consule Planco*, in the days of Brigadier-General Spofforth-Spalding.'

As the train rode along an embankment through the shimmering paddy fields on the last lap of our journey to Deolali, James said: 'I bought an English language paper on Poonah Station last night. Too dark to read in here then. But there was some interesting news when I looked at it this morning.'

He passed it over.

'Riots in Bombay,' Rory said.

There had been rumours, from whatever source, that Independence might be postponed, after all, until 1948. Dockers were striking in Bombay; rabble was looting; British troops, about to embark, were on the verge of mutiny as ships were delayed and the prospect of Blighty receded.

Having digested all this, Rory retired to our lavatory.

'This is not what Rory needs,' I said to James. 'He wants an immediate passage.'

'And a day or two in Bombay to sort his gonorrhoea out first.'

Rory came back from the loo with face twisted. 'Like broken safety pins,' he said.

In Deolali there was almost a state of standing room only. The three of us and three more shared a bell tent. We ate in the junior officers' mess by shifts. There was always a meal of some kind in session. The days went past. No leave was given as there was nowhere safe to go.

The Indian barman said: 'There is very much drinking here among those who are afraid they will never be embarked on a ship. You are lucky that the authorities have not closed the bar. Such closure was indeed ordered, but our contractor, Mr Lal Moti, who enjoys much profit from selling delicious Indian drinks, made a present to the good commandant sahib, and the order was most swiftly countermanded.'

'Thank God for bribery,' I said. 'Where would we be without it?'

'Sober,' said Rory, who wasn't.

'Bribery,' said James thoughtfully. 'There is a time and place for everything.'

He drained his drink and left. Twenty minutes later he was back.

'There is an officer in the Dental Corps,' he said to Rory, 'who is willing to be consulted in a private capacity.'

'Dental Corps? How can he help?'

'They do a lot of medicine before they get on to teeth. Now, then. It is well over a month since we were on leave – in a day or two it will be time for your Wassermann. My man can get your blood tested in the medical centre . . . presenting the sample in a false name and saying that he's spotted suspicious lesions on the chap's gums.'

Rory went very red. 'Oh I say,' he said feebly, 'surely nobody — '

' — Don't tick, Rory. Just come with me for your dental appointment.'

A few days later we were informed that 14477929 Private Pugh, RP, who had in fact been buried a few weeks earlier of bilharzia but whose name still passed current in the confusion, was not infected with primary specific disease, a medical euphemism then in vogue for the Great Pox presumably on the principle that polite nomenclature – 'the Kindly Ones' – mitigates the menace of disagreeable personae – 'the

Furies'. By much the same token syphilis was affectionately called by the soldiery 'the Bombay Boater-Riband' or, more commonly, 'the Red Beret', the latter term much annoying members of the Parachute Regiment.

'It cost me a packet,' said James, 'but I couldn't bear to see Rory in such horrible suspense.'

'He's still got his clap-clap-clap to cope with.'

'No. The dentist has come up with another diagnosis. He says Rory has a discharge, easily cured by a few pills and caused by sexual strain. He just did it far too often with that wicked old woman.'

'A witch,' I said, 'just as you told me some time back. She must be, or she could never have enticed him to that extent. How old would you say she was? According to Rory, she had an affair with that dying Cornet of Cavalry in 1905. She was a young married woman then, so she must be sixty or a bit more now . . . forty years on.'

'The morning before we caught the train from Bangalore,' said James, 'I went to the OTS library and looked for her husband in old Army lists and books of reference. Brigadier-General Spofforth-Spalding was born in 1857. Educated at Haileybury and Trinity Hall, Cambridge, he was commissioned as ensign or second lieutenant in the Sussex Regiment in 1878, transferred to the Indian Army (Rajputana Rifles) in 1885 in the rank of lieutenant, and married Gertrude May Atwood (his first and only wife), daughter of Lieutenant-Colonel Charles McGuiness Atwood (Mysore Horse Artillery) shortly after he was gazetted as captain in 1887 . . . the lady being the same age as himself, which is to say thirty.'

I did a little mental arithmetic.

'So that when Rory was knocking her, she was knocking ninety?'

'Right,' said James. 'A witch, as you agree with me. It is, I think, the kindest description. One of the cordials which witches use to preserve themselves is the seminal fluid of vigorous young men, both as a tonic and as an unguent of external application. No doubt she made the most of Rory as a donor; and no wonder he contracted strain in his dispenser.'

'But surely, if Rory was shafting her properly — '

' — I don't think we need go into detail. Witches have their own methods of ordering these matters.'

NB Those interested in the persistence of oestrus in the female should refer to the Satires of Hipponax of Ephesus and Smyrna (*floruit c.* 540 BC), who composed in the *Scazon* or 'limping' iambic. His wit was so vicious that it drove the artist Bupalus and his catamite Athenis to suicide. Bupalus had carved a statue mocking the extreme ugliness of the poet. In revenge, Hipponax wrote a Satire (unfortunately lost) in which he stated that Bupalus' mother received all male applicants for a nugatory charge until the age of ninety-three and conceived Bupalus himself at the age of eighty-seven. As a witch, she had an extensive knowledge of philtres and lotions, but made several serious errors in their application: thus she ingested a fertility potion in mistake for an aphrodisiac, and so was got with Bupalus, and she made some similar blunder when muffing his abortion. (See *Horace, Epode vi, 1.14*)

ii) *The Shadowy Coast*

'When I was a cadet at Bangalore,' I said to O, 'we had neither the time nor the money to come to magic places like this.'

The sea lapped at the steps of the temple. Stone figures above the landing stage gazed eastward, supercilious and indifferent. A stubby lady spread herself for a bored god and settled on to his eternally erect penis.

'Pity. If you had been able to come here then,' said O, 'it would all have been genuine.'

'Genuine?'

'Forty-one years ago, when you were a cadet, it would have been simply a temple on a beach, washed by the waves of the ocean. Pilgrims and worshippers, the legitimate visitors, would have been here, immersing themselves in the cleansing waters. The idle among them would have dawdled on the sands. The philosophers would have philosophised, the moralists have moralised; the artists would have rendered versions of the scene; the poets would have composed stanzas, and the priests would have assessed their behaviour – opining to anyone that would listen how far that person's activity was assisting him to transcend the transitory or preventing him from doing so.

'But now,' said O, 'there are no pilgrims and no priests, because the place is no longer holy. It has lost its legitimate function and with that function its legitimate familiars, human or divine. Instead, there is just a sweaty mass of middle-class tourists. In the old days even the activities which the priests deprecated would have been significant. The idlers would have dreamt of the ocean's depths; the sentiments of the poets and moralisers, even if hostile, would never have been trivial. Everyone without exception would have known and appreciated what he was looking at, would have understood that here was a precinct in which one might eventually learn how to free oneself from the wheel of material existence, should one so wish.

'But now . . . what do we see on these sacred sands but the oozing and ever spreading garbage of profanity made flesh? Pallid, pampered and misshapen flesh informed by ignorant and apathetic spirit. Which is the more disgusting? The greed of the natives who have conveyed these cargoes of human detritus here in stinking juggernauts? Or the avaricious yet feeble-minded tourist, eternally complaining of bad value and ill-treatment, yet ever more wickedly gulled and mis-informed?'

At least it was a change from his usual threnody, which was to the effect that having served his country as a soldier for thirty years, he was now thanklessly discarded and the target of newfangled moral contempt. This theme he renewed, a day or two later, at Fort St George in Madras. He began in the Church – 'No one will erect worthy monuments like these in honour of our comrades of Kenya and Korea' – and went banging on till we reached the first floor of the museum. There he saw a portrait of Warren Hastings in which Hastings' head was sunk so far between his shoulders that one could hardly see anything of his face beneath the doll's eyes and bruiser's ears.

'I'd sooner not have a memorial like that,' he said.

'You won't.'

'Surely they could have done better for such a magnificent servant of his country?'

'Of the East India Company.'

'Which,' said O, 'was British. Warren Hastings was a superb patriot.'

'Nationalist,' I said; 'in so far as he wasn't merely a careerist.'

'As you well know,' said O, 'the nation's affairs are most efficiently advanced by men who are activated by personal pride, as well as pride in their country, and by rational desire of personal gain.'

'Certainly. Churchill was an excellent example – at least if we are to judge from Mary Churchill's book about her parents.'

'Then why sneer at Warren Hastings?'

'I am not,' I said, 'sneering at anybody. I just like to use accurate terms when describing men and motives.'

We climbed into our coach to be taken to an urban Indian Temple. It seemed to be divided into a series of small courtyards of an attractive pattern, which were, however, disfigured by much casual filth and obtrusive statues coloured like Liquorice Allsorts. In one courtyard there was a squatting bride, in the midst of some rite which would last, we were told, for the next week. In the alley between this courtyard and the next was a prominent advertisement in luminous mauve for an Oriental Bank.

'The Pasha would have enjoyed that,' said O. 'What happened to Tel-Hotel?'

'It vanished. About eighteen years ago. 1970 or '71, in the autumn, if I remember.'

'So Hamilton and Hamish lost their money? Or rather, Hamilton's money.'

This was another of O's habits: to switch suddenly to a discussion of events a great while previous and discuss them as if they had occurred that morning, expecting one to remember every detail as meticulously as he did.

'I was sorry to hear that Hamish and Hamilton had split up,' said O. 'I don't care much for marriages, but I found that one amusing. What went wrong?'

'Drink.'

'Yes. They did rather like a drop. And the Pasha. And your boy, Adam.'

'We all did,' I said.

'The Pasha,' O said with lingering affection. 'Martin Stevens, who subsequently became Member of Parliament for Fulham; very conscientious, I'm told, and much appreciated by his constituents, and all the while a common swindler.'

'In the end he was swindled himself,' I said.

'Pray expand . . .'

'By one of his best friends, scion of a well-known toothpaste family. Classical Trollopean treachery – dishonouring a bill, or the modern equivalent, and leaving the guarantor – Martin – to pay up.'

'Biter bit?'

'For far more than he'd ever bitten anyone else for. One hundred grand. Still an important sum when it happened.'

'And then,' said O, 'Martin was bitten again . . . or so I read in the paper. By some insect-eating plant, in Africa. What an impertinence the thing had – biting a British MP. Farewell, Pasha; Pasha, farewell. It was an education to have known him. Oh, the whirligig of fortune . . . Didn't you say that Hamilton later gave Hamish some shares in something or other, thinking they were as worthless as the ones in Tel-Hotel, only to see them jump to thirty times their original value almost over night?'

'Yes,' I said crossly. 'And Adam has become quite an appealing artist by transforming Provençal farmhouses into nursery fantasies. A lot of unlikely things can happen in nearly twenty years.'

There was a flurry of gongs. A party of painted androgynes capered past to press some service on the embattled bride.

'That Christmas in Venice,' said O, 'you'd just started writing that television thing, *The Pallisers.*'

'Yes. I still get money for repeats of the serial in obscure corners of the earth. The trouble is that the payments are made on a scale devised when sterling was worth ten times what it is now. Another trouble is that the producer, Martin Lismore, whom I liked very much and might have given me a lot more work, was killed in a motor-smash by a drunken yob. And yet another trouble is that most dramatic television programmes are now co-productions, so that instead of writing the bloody things one spends one's time waiting for "creative" Americans to decide whether to put up the cash and then quarrelling with them about their imbecile notions of action and dialogue.'

'These are no thoughts for a temple. The Hindu religion encourages you to disengage yourself from worldly concerns.'

'Which, I suppose, explains that prominent advertisement for a bank.'

'According to that bit near the bottom,' said O, 'the bank specialises in administering the estates of senior citizens who divest themselves both of their authority and their knickers, and go walk-about with a begging bowl. Apparently rich and successful Indians quite often do that . . . as senility starts looming.'

'Not a bad idea. At least one would be spared the horrors of co-productions with creative Americans.'

'In England the climate isn't suitable for going around naked. Anyhow, you'd be sent to prison.'

'That might solve a lot of problems.'

At the entrance to the temple when we retrieved our footwear, I said, 'Why do they make one take off one's shoes to walk about in a garbage heap?'

'The garbage, like all other material phenomena, disappears without trace if you concentrate on spiritual realities. It is a question of controlling one's vision.'

A bicycle rickshaw went *ting-a-ling* down the street.

'I suppose it's an improvement,' said O, 'on having some poor wretch pulling the thing. But somehow . . . the old fashion was far more attractive.'

In Bangalore we stayed at the hotel where I had attended a tennis party in 1947 and played with Sydney Bryanstone on lawns of lovingly tended grass. The hotel was now fifteen storeys high, with a leisure complex which had tennis courts of some rebarbative colloidal substance. We were greeted by simpering bearers, who hung garlands which smelt and felt like dishclothes round our necks.

'The Americans like it,' explained O. 'They think it means that the Indians are happy to see them.'

I walked with him to the old OTS cricket ground. Unlike the tennis courts at the hotel, the wicket was still of grass; but the old pavilion had gone and the entire ground was surrounded by lowering stands, where once there had been rows of slender trees through which there was a view of distant shrines among straggling copses of casuarina.

'It's no good being sentimental,' said O: 'this is now one of the Mysore State Grounds. It was bound to be developed.'

'It was always one of the Mysore State Grounds as well as ours. We were very proud of that. But in those days nobody needed piles of cement to watch the Mysore XI from.'

'They'd think they were being cheated of something if they didn't have them now.'

On the way back to the hotel we looked back down the avenue.

'Those stands look like a prison,' I said. 'Where's the entrance? We used to cycle straight in through a wooden gateway without a gate.'

'Couldn't have that these days. Some one might walk in and dig up the pitch. Nothing like egalitarianism for giving spiteful notions to those that haven't come to be *quite* as equal as some others.'

We waited to cross the honking, stinking avenue to the hotel.

'When we first came to Bangalore,' I said while we waited, and then waited, for a pause in the traffic, 'they still thought that after we were commissioned we might be in India for some time before the British Army beat a final retreat. They even thought that some of us might be commissioned into the Indian Army, to assist the process of transition. So we had Munshis to teach us Urdu. Four or five of us would go to one Munshi and sit round him like disciples. The Munshis were dressed in spotless white tunics and breeches. When they arrived, they came in a cluster of fluttering white and gradually separated, each to his position on the verandah of the building in which were the lecture rooms. When we came up to our respective Munshi, we halted and saluted, and said, "*Salaam*, Munshi Sahib"; and they rose and put the palms of their hands together, and said, "*Salaam*, Officer Cadet Sahib", or later on, when they knew us better, "*Salaam*, Raven Sahib" or "*Salaam*, Parkes Sahib", as the case might be.

'In a word, O, there was courtesy between us and often, as the weeks went on, affection. Then, when the authorities realised that we would not be staying in India long enough to justify the trouble and expense of teaching us Urdu, the Munshis were given notice. One morning, the Munshi whom I attended, with three of my particular friends, said to us at the end of the lesson, "Today has been our last time together, Officer Cadet Sahibs, so we must say a small prayer for parting. I shall pray that you will remember your Munshi long after you have forgotten the words he taught you. And I hope that you will pray that I shall remember you, long after the British have gone away from India."

'Then we all lowered our heads and prayed. After a few seconds we rose, put on our headgear, and saluted. "*Salaam*, Munshi Sahib", we said. And he rose and put his hands together: "*Salaam*, Officer Cadet Sahibs", he said.

'Ever since then I have remembered him, as you have just heard. I wonder whether he still remembers me. I wonder just how he fits into the new Bangalore, and whether he preferred the old.'

'Of course he didn't,' said O. 'He became a figure of importance in

63

the university, and is almost certainly long since dead, because of the faulty sanitation, which they say has much deteriorated since your time. Dead like all the others of whom you have told me, the rickshaw wallahs that pulled the cadets home in illicit couples after dinner in the Officers' and O/Cadets' Club in the cricket pavilion, or the bearers and syces who danced to the drums on the far side of the road, opposite the cadets' quarters. And nobody calls anybody "Sahib" any more: they just dump stale flowers round your neck when you arrive and wish you good riddance when you go. There has been, I see, a very nasty accident, and the traffic will stop for just long enough for us to cross the road.'

When we had reached the other side, not without peril as most drivers totally ignored the accident, O said: 'I can see that Bangalore has saddened you. What a good thing our group is only staying here the one night. Tomorrow we shall be taken to Goa. They say that the coast there is paradisiac.'

'By which I suppose they mean aphrodisiac.'

'There are stories, certainly, of several kinds of snake in the garden.'

At Goa wanton, naked cherubs scampered about the private beach which belonged to our palatial hotel and shamelessly fondled each other, wandering away into the dunes in goatish groups. Behind the dunes baroque churches and chapels crumbled in the forest. In the scabby bungalows nearby, divorced wives of English dons and lawyers injected themselves with heroin and nagged at their twelve-year-old daughters until they threw their virginities away on beachcombing Indian youths of the lowest conceivable caste.

'Such things would not have happened under the Raj,' said O.

'Goa had nothing to do with the Raj. Goa was Portuguese. Hence all the fuss about that foul man, Xavier. You can't imagine the Protestant Raj would have allowed his corpse to be placed on show in a glass coffin – even if it is miraculously preserved?'

'I'm told they fetch him out every ten years,' said O crossly, 'and tote him about through crowds of howling and prostrate Indian converts. But apparently he's had his last outing, as the cadaver is finally falling apart . . . and the next dose of fresh air will bring it to dust.'

'Sludge,' I said. 'Dust to dust is a euphemism. Corpses turn into something much nastier than dust.'

' "Golden lads and girls all trudge, as chimney-sweepers, into sludge",' O misquoted by way of experiment. 'Somehow, it lacks the charm of the original.'

A horde of jolly children ran past us and into the trees, two of them brandishing syringes.

'But of course in the end,' O went on, 'whatever it is, dust or sludge, simply disappears. Along with the worms that eat it. Only the bone is left – "the steadfast and enduring bone".'

'You seem full of poetry today.'

'Mortality,' said O, 'is richly illustrated in poetry. It is a very quotable topic.'

'Granted. But what set you off?'

'Your mention of that brute, Xavier. I suppose we'd better go and see his celebrated tomb while we're here. The architecture which surrounds it is rather choice. There are two large churches, one of which is a cathedral, within spitting distance of each other. I rather think that Xavier is in the one which isn't a cathedral. Everything else in the area was burnt down to destroy a plague of rats. But now that there is no danger of plague, there is a beach nearby even rortier and druggier than this one. If you ask me, those old plague rats were far preferable to what's arrived in that part since. The scum of Europe and America turn up there. The Indians put up with them out of greed for the hard currency.'

'One can't really blame them,' I said: 'India is rather a poor country.'

'Hindus at least,' said O, 'shouldn't mind that. I know there are a lot of Catholics in Goa, but the majority are Hindus, and Hindus should not be thinking of money at all. They'd be much happier if they didn't.'

'We all would, but we can't quite seem to manage it. Come to that, we'd all be happier dead. The point about money is that it buys agreeable commodities and so gives us the illusion that life is worth living. It promotes activities which make us forget our fear of death.'

'But why do we fear death if, according to you, we shall all be happier when dead?'

'That's what amused Lucretius,' I said. 'He observed that some people were made so miserable by the fear of death – if they couldn't get enough money or pleasure or power to help them forget it – that they killed themselves to cure their misery.'

'Thus yielding themselves up to that very thing the thought of which had caused their misery?'

'I suppose they thought that the actuality of death might be more tolerable than the prospect . . . that it might not be so bad once one had broken the ice, so to speak.'

'Or that they might as well confront it now as later? Couldn't they understand that death is just total oblivion and therefore totally harmless?'

'That's what Lucretius tried to tell them.'

Shrill sounds of pleasure came over the dunes from the forest.

'But of course,' said O, 'they wouldn't believe him. Too vain, apart from anything else. "How could *I* ever cease to exist?" There is no limit to human silliness. I once had a friend, a schoolmaster, who said that he was looking forward to the life after death so much that it was only this that kept him living.'

We walked over the dunes, looking down on the white satin beach and the rough blue silk of the sea.

'My schoolmaster chum,' O pursued, 'insisted that if he ever ceased to believe in the life after death he would commit suicide immediately in sheer despair. People do not appear to think or argue very logically on the subject of death. It is clearly a matter suited to poetry rather than to prose.'

' "The iniquity of oblivion blindly scattereth her poppy." What about that for threnody in prose? Courtesy of Sir T Browne.'

'Magnificent sound,' said O: 'no sense.'

'The sense is very plain. It means that death is a random affair and so is subsequent memorial.'

'You remember Paddy Philips in the First Battalion?'

'Vividly. He was covered by black hairs as thick as a bear. I once saw him in a shower. He said – on another occasion – that I was a rotten officer.'

'How perceptive of him,' said O. 'That child just taking its clothes off has a beautiful face but hideous legs. So often the case.'

'What about Paddy Philips?'

'He married a mature lady from the WVS. They were blissfully happy for a few months. Then Paddy died at thirty-seven of a heart attack. Malcolm Carr also died pretty young of a heart attack – leaving, like Paddy, a loving and lovable wife.'

'Your conclusion?'

'Death is not random at all. It is one more instance of the malice of God – who kills the happy and leaves the wretched to live indefinitely.'

There was a scream, not of pleasure, from the forest.

'This is a very agreeable spot,' said O, 'but now we'd better walk away from it. We don't want to be mixed up in any inquiries. They might not let us catch our aeroplane home. So left, right, left, old bean. Not *too* fast, in case we are noticed.'

'I shouldn't mind staying in India a little longer than we'd expected. No harm in being asked a few questions when one genuinely knows nothing.'

'In no time at all you'd find yourself in a cell,' said O. 'Someone would say we should have stopped those children going into the woods when we saw the syringes; that we were to blame for what had happened. And even if they let us out of the slammer, we'd never get out of India.'

'What nonsense you talk.'

'Our tour would long since have departed,' said O in a sing-song voice, 'and when you are our age you can't survive in India unless you're with a tour. You haven't the energy to do all the booking and bribing. After a time you cease to care; your money runs out, you are too slothful to send for more and even if you do make the effort, the remittance is subject to the malversation of Indian postal officials. Eventually you cease to eat and to wash, your clothes rot on your body and your brain rots in your head, then you die and decompose, not nearly as slowly as Xavier. So we shall walk away, now, from whatever unpleasantness has occurred among those trees, and rejoin our respectable group, before it is too late, in our luxury hotel.'

PART THREE

Hellas

i Athens

For all the Athenians and strangers which were there spent their time in nothing else, but either to tell, or to hear some new thing.

Acts of the Apostles: Ch 17:v 21

These days, Athens is the nastiest and most polluted city in Europe – in the world. It wasn't quite so foul in 1984, when I spent a week there with a chum who had a flat which looked out on to the woods of Lycabettos. Although the trees were suffering from a kind of arboreal scurvy, they weren't absolutely dead, as I expect they are by now.

Anyhow, despite the noisy, scummy road immediately under my chum's windows and the decaying woods on the other side of it, it was fun staying with him for a number of reasons: his knowledge of Athenian antiquities, cinemas and eateries (one can hardly call them restaurants); his deadly deadpan malice at the expense of our common acquaintance, and his enthusiasm for two-handed games of chance, such as backgammon and gin rummy. But what I chiefly recall from this visit is a process of remembering: how any site or sight I saw provoked a melancholy comparison between what I was seeing now, in March of 1984, and what I had seen when I first came to Athens with Burgo Partridge a quarter of a century before . . . when the forest on Lycabettos was still healthy and Athens was still an agreeable if unremarkable city, provincial in size and air, of modest and seemly dwellings, orange-tiled and ochre-walled, instead of a huge, honking, ordurous Gehenna of smouldering streets, proletarian breeding-boxes, and brutal granite blocks.

Burgo and I arrived a few days before Christmas in 1959. The King of the Hellenes was on his throne; officer cadets of all three armed services walked the handsome avenues which led in and out of Constitution Square, gilt-sheathed daggers slung at their sides; clusters of balloons were released into the pale-blue sky and rose until they attained oneness with the empyrean.

'We shall sit down here,' said Burgo, having spotted a tin-roofed café in the Zappeion Gardens, which marched with the gardens of the palace, 'and have a drink in honour of Christmas, though neither of us, thank God, sets any store by Christ.'

Burgo ordered noxious ouzo. I ordered Fix, the national beer, thin as canary's piss but at that time the only brand available.

'Celebrating Christmas at home in Hungerford,' said Burgo, 'will be Frances my mother, Ralph my father, and their guest Isobel Strachey, whose legs are as thin as the stem of a hock glass and were said, in her youth, to open as easily and as often as a pair of nail scissors. But her youth has long since given way to what Horace calls "*canities morosa*", sour grey senescence, to conceal which she has a special hairdo which she can ill-afford even though it is only annual, before proceeding to my parents at Hungerford every Christmas. She has a fantasy, you see, about being in the train of one of the Three Kings and honourably strives, at this season, to be looking at her best. She forgets that these only had men in their entourage, noblemen and knights and esquires – witness all the pretty pictures by Sandro Botticelli *et al*. The only lady present was the Virgin; no other females, but of course lots of ogling pages. Isobel's daughter, Charlotte, looks like an ogling page. She was once married to Hamilton Glott.'

The ouzo and its predecessors were making Burgo inconsequent. To set him back on course I said, 'I know that very well, Burgo; Hamilton, as you may recall, is my publicity agent, and it was he that introduced me to Charlotte, while she was still his wife. As I told you at the time, I very much fancied her, but when she had done with Hamilton she appeared to prefer Peter Jenkins to myself.'

'Jenkins. The pink parrot of the *Manchester Guardian*. Charlotte says that he was the first man that ever made her come. I was brought up with Charlotte, you know. *We* did not come. We played together innocently in infancy and pre-pubescence. Not in pubescence, when presumably we might have come, for by that time I had been sent away to school.' He took a gulp of ouzo. 'But school is another story. Where was I before I digressed?'

'You were at your home at Ham Spray, with Ralph and Frances and Isobel, who are there celebrating Christmas.'

'Ah. My apologies. You hardly know them really. Let me explain them all.'

He gazed up at a yellow balloon which had stopped ascending and was hovering, at a height of a hundred yards, over our café.

'O yellow star of Bethlehem,' said Burgo, and tinkled his glass with a teaspoon which the previous incumbents had left lying about. 'Perhaps I am the Christ-child, waiting for the three Kings, who will not conceivably allow Isobel, even with her special hairdo, to follow in their wake, but might very well accept Charlotte as an honorary and delectable pageboy; though Charlotte will have none of them, Kings or no, as she is exclusively obsessed, just now, with Jenkers' stubby little stalk.' He tinkled so impatiently that the glass broke. This mishap restored Burgo's concentration. 'But do not permit me to stray any more,' he said, as I shook my head to warn away the approaching waiter. 'I shall now my tale unfold, as I have promised, of Frances and Ralph and Isobel and Charlotte, though not much of it concerns Isobel, except in so far as she was Charlotte's mother.

'My father, Ralph Partridge was an oarsman and a warrior, who gloried in the rank of major and won a Military Cross in the war of 1914. With this golden if philistine youth, Lytton Strachey (no less) fell in love; but meanwhile my father pined for cruel Carrington, the painter, who, in her turn, was sick with desire for bearded Strachey. Death gathered Carrington; time and chance turned Lytton Strachey to other infatuations; and my father was left free for my mother, Frances, who taught him socialism, pacifism, Luddism, and literature. He lived at Ham Spray, writing one article a week for the *New Statesman*, in the intervals of gambling cleverly for quick and marginal returns on the Stock Exchange. From these activities he took leisure to make long tours through Europe with my mother and Gerald Brenan, tours during which they deplored the condition of the peasantry as seen through the windows of their motor car and discussed what other people ought to be doing about it over dinner in the best hotel. Then I was born, a potential nuisance, but luckily there were, in those days, plenty of Spock-trained nannies with whom I could be safely deposited for liberal and non-repressive potty-training and later, of course, a tempting choice of crank schools to which I could be sent whenever I became annoying or superfluous.

'Although the 1939 war rather cramped my parents' style, they lived pretty comfortably at Ham Spray, making amusing jokes at the expense of those who were risking life or ghastly trauma to defend them, and contriving ever more ingenious schemes to "evacuate" myself to a safe distance from Hungerford. Meanwhile, their friends John and Isobel Strachey, not to be confused with lanky Lytton, had produced little Charlotte, with whom I played unhappily through the long, hot summers. My trouble was that I was convinced that nobody loved me, and this for the best of reasons: I was uniquely unlovable. At the age of nine I dug a large hole and sent Charlotte, in whose house I was staying, to fetch her parents to admire it. "What a lovely *hole*, Burgo," drawled Isobel; "whatever is it *for?*" "To put Ralph and Frances in," I replied. For they always made me call them "Ralph" and "Frances", though I longed to call them "Mummy" and "Daddy" like an ordinary child: one more reason why I was so horrible. On this particular occasion, John Strachey, who was busy thinking of himself, ignored my remark while Isobel laughed at it. Since they were meant to be outraged, their respective indifference and merriment infuriated me so much that I hit Charlotte with the blade of my shovel and laid her forehead open . . . after which, of course, I had to be sent home where, in consequence, I was loved less than ever.

'When I grew up,' said Burgo, 'I had large warts all over my body, greasy black hair, the complexion of an ill-nourished half-caste, and exceedingly smelly feet. Only one woman ever found me attractive, and she had an erectile clitoris, which I adored but dared not caress, in case she thought I was a latent homosexual. I developed a furtive manner; I slobbered when I smoked, which my nerves compelled me to do incessantly; I walked like Baron Frankenstein's monster at his first attempt; Charlotte called me "Caliban". Anyone who saw me became immediately hostile and suspicious: Englishmen thought I was a Jew; Jews thought I was an Arab; Arabs thought I was an Indian, Hindu of course; Hindus thought I was an Untouchable; Untouchables thought I was an Unseeable; Unseeables thought I was a tax-gatherer or a money-lender; money-lenders thought – indeed very well knew – that I was a natural and gutless gull, and charged me excessive interest.'

'Surely your parents didn't keep you so short that you had to go to the money-lenders?'

'No. They put me in charge of my own money affairs at the age of sixteen, making very liberal arrangements – to alleviate their guilt. But every now and then I overspent my income, and no bank manager would give me an overdraft of more than twopence, although I had ample security, because they thought I looked like a terrorist.' (As indeed the British Patrols thought when we later visited Cyprus.) 'So I had to go to the money-lenders,' Burgo continued, 'who charged me sixty per cent, instead of the usual fifty.'

'But sixty per cent is illegal.'

'I was a Lesser Breed, without the law, as Kipling has it, and so forfeited its protection. Nobody gave me credit even when I did something worthwhile. I wrote a lovingly researched book about orgies*, but everyone said its success was due to Charlotte because she persuaded Hamilton Glott (to whom, by this time, she was married) to publicise it, and to my parents because they persuaded their friends Cyril Connolly and Raymond Mortimer to review it; and to Gerald Brennan because he persuaded Heywood Hill to stack a special table with it and display blown-up copies of Cyril's review all over his shop. He even conned Evelyn Waugh into buying a copy, which Waugh accidentally left in White's, where it was found by Bob Boothby . . . who was excited by one of the pictures and told Maurice Bowra who told John Sparrow who told Noël Annan, thus winning the book a high reputation, which my father said was a fluke. I was, my father said, a wretchedly bad writer, ignorant, superficial, clumsy and jejune. I wish the Germans had shot him in the Great War.'

'Then you wouldn't be here now.'

'I shouldn't care.'

'I should,' I said, meaning it.

I loved Burgo; not physically, for no one, except the lady with the erectile clitoris, ever did that; but with my heart. All the same, I

A History of Orgies by Burgo Partridge. Published 1959 by Anthony Blond. Second-hand copies are still available in the Charing Cross Road.

laughed as loudly as everyone else at the manner of his early death. He was talking to Charlotte on the telephone. Charlotte was inviting herself and Jenkins, for whom she had now left Glott, to a drink at Burgo's house in Cadogan Square. 'You're sure it's not a bore, Burgo,' Charlotte wheedled. 'Oh no,' said Burgo, and dropped dead of a ruptured aorta. Hence the story, widely current for some years, that Charlotte had bored Burgo to death over the telephone. The story was dropped after Charlotte became ill of some devilish disease of the blood. She had to have her beautiful blonde hair cut off, so that she had a stubbly pate and (with the drug they gave her) bulbous cheeks. A few weeks before she died she said to some of us at dinner, 'If there's anything you want to do, do it now, while you're still here. That's what I'm still here to tell you.' Glott, with whom she had long been reconciled, took her to Kew just before she died. 'I never came with you,' she said. 'I know,' said Glott. 'I came with Peter; but after a while I didn't. I was going to try with Simon; but then my illness happened.' I wish I had had the chance to be Charlotte's lover. I always longed to kiss the little silver cunt at the fork of the fourth-former's thighs. (I once saw this ensemble, when we were bathing naked at Ham Spray.) I dream about and sometimes masturbate about it, even now.

But I must go back to Burgo, half-drunk in the Zappeion Gardens. Together we enjoyed Athens very much that Christmas of 1959 particularly, and perversely, the Roman remains rather than the Greek. We walked up Lycabettos one afternoon and talked of the disgusting food in Athens and of my early sexual experiences at my prep school. Burgo would not believe that it is possible to come (the feeling without the emission) before one reaches puberty. At last I convinced him, describing the way in which my little prick had 'juddered'. He was intrigued, though not in the least interested in little boys, and then became jealous: 'Why didn't *I* come before puberty?' he said crossly. 'Think what I've missed, and missed forever*.'

After this typical instance of Burgo's resentment, we had Turkish coffee at a stall about half way up Lycabettos – in those days you were

*Had Burgo lived to have an operation for the prostate, he could have experienced precisely that type of orgasm – far more exciting (*crede experto*) than the usual adult performance. In this connection, see Ludovic Kennedy's account in *On My Way to the Club*.

forbidden to go further because of a military installation of some kind – and then walked down again. As we walked, we looked down on the Arch of Hadrian, beyond the Zappeion Gardens, and the Tower of the Winds away to the West, while Burgo made some more spiteful but oddly loving jokes about his father and mother. The sun shone in the pale-blue sky, and when we came to the Plazeia Syntagmatos we watched some morose cadets, whose leave was to end on the morrow, stroll slowly to and fro with their hands resting on the hilts of their daggers. I gazed up, as I have always loved to ever since, at the balloons which dwindled and then, with a final flicker, vanished and became one with God who is the Good and the Beautiful, so Plato and his disciples tell us.

All that is what I was looking for in Athens in 1984, and no longer found.

ii) Scheria: the godlike Phaeacians

*And therein grow trees, high and abounding, pears
and pomegranates and coloured apples, sweet figs
and olives in abundance. Of these the bounty
fades not nor fails in winter nor in summer, but
quickens through all the year; and ever does the
West Wind as it blows bring to blossom some fruits
and to ripeness others, pear upon pear, apple upon
apple, cluster upon cluster, fig upon fig.*

Homer: *Odyssey; BK VII, 11. 114 to 121. Trans: SR*

'So who's going to be there?' said Benjamin Crud as he, Adam and I, in Adam's grunting and grating Renault 5 (or was it 4?), struggled up the stony way to Hamilton and Hamish's new house on Corfu.

'Martin Stevens, for one,' I said. 'He was with us in Venice the Christmas before last – when Hamish tricked Hamilton into coming here to buy this house.'

'Having promised Hamilton dinner with Lord Thurso,' said Adam, 'though he knew very well that Thurso would be gone by the time they arrived.'

'What *was* here,' I said, 'was the shell of a house at the top of this hill. I'm told that Hamish has done it up brilliantly.'

'With Hamilton's money,' said Benj Crud.

'Difficult to think of a better way of using it. Hamilton would only have pissed it down the gutter if Hamish had let him keep it.'

And as it turned out Hamish had indeed used the money well. The house, ruined by neglect during the war and many years after, had been that of a superior peasant farmer. Set on the spine of a north-south ridge between two abundant valleys in the northern bulge of Corcyra, it looked out over farmland and a lush new golf course to the West, as far as a low rocky ridge which barely hid the sea and through which wound the river that would later debouch on to the beach where Odysseus had surprised Nausicaä and her maidens at play nearly three thousand years before, while to the East the house commanded a long view of hills and dales rich in various forests, which rolled to the suburbs of the capital, Corfu. One could see beyond the city and across a strait to

Epiros and cruel Albania, to white mountains which rose above bare hills which rose above an iron coast. To the West, then, one looked towards soft scenes of pretty legends; to the East towards a Barbary that, by contrast, increased one's pleasure in the seemly and comfortable house which Hamish had made with Hamilton's money. To the North and South the range which the house straddled was covered with ranked pines and crowding olives; these obscured the view to the South, but far away to the North the mass of Pantocrator rose clear of the treetops and lowered over all.

Round the house, which was named Opsiopoulos (possibly translatable as The Place of Vision), Hamish had planted a garden of shrubs to the West and North and an orchard to the East and South. There were cypress trees which partly hid the house from prying faces down in the valley to the West and surrounded a tiny chapel, like courtiers flanking a canopied throne. Some way beneath the house, on a plateau in the western downslope of the ridge, was an abandoned convent, from which a former owner of Opsiopoulos had abducted a novice who, unlike the nun in Noël Coward's ballad, had not resented it. Unfortunately she herself had been resented and butchered by the owner's heir, who mistrusted the probable fertility of her profane youth. At some seasons, so they said and still say to those who will listen, her ghost walks and weeps in the courtyard separating the northern and southern sections of the building.

Already present in Opsiopoulos in that autumn of the early Seventies were not only Hamish, Hamilton and Martin Stevens, but also a blithe and diminutive huntsman and amateur jockey, heir presumptive to a fine marquessate, called Guy Nevill and his leman, a lank-haired authoress with a lamp-post figure, Philippa Puller.

Now, at this time I was mildly infatuated with Hamish; moderately attracted by Philippa; responsible for Adam; under certain obligations to Hamilton; respectful of Guy for his presumed and future seigneury; and amused by Martin, the kindly and obese crook. Of Benjamin Crud, then a full decade and a half away from his hankering after Christ and the Roman Catholic Church, as demonstrated in the cathedral on Torcello and described in the early pages of this book, I was definitely wary. I did not much like his pictures, except for the smaller landscapes; and I did not at all like the saurian and grovelling lechery in which he sought to involve and envelop me. I therefore had, you might say, complications in my life, but only minor ones, with the possible exception of Adam; and I decided that the best thing to do while at Opsiopoulos was to leave Adam, now legally of age, to entertain himself – for after all he must learn sometime – and to occupy myself in isolation from the rest, save for the common uses of civility, by reading two very long, important and demanding books, which I had been meaning to read for some time – Richardson's *Clarissa* and Spengler's *Decline of the West*. These I was going to read in tandem, so to speak, and I carried them with a folding chair on the first morning after my arrival to a point of look-out over the western valley, and there settled to serious study.

Not for long. Adam, who was at this stage of his career a 'poet' having not yet got round to being a painter, came to me with a long list of commonplace words, the meanings of which they had neglected to teach him at Bedales. Hamish then came to suggest that I should assist in a nasty piece of weeding, from which I was able to excuse myself on a plea of contract – for had I not agreed to pay for the construction of a large marble table, at which the whole company up to twelve persons might lunch al fresco in the courtyard, on the absolute understanding that no form of menial labour in the house or garden might ever be required of me? After a vicious spat, Hamish, who disliked honouring contracts when it did not suit him, flouncily withdrew with his rather pointed nose held high in the air, sniffing and muttering about people who thought they were too important to share in common tasks merely because they had achieved minuscule literary reputations. The total lack of critical response of any kind to the two novels he himself had written was at that time (and for long after) angrily infecting his swollen self-esteem.

After Hamish came Hamilton, who wanted someone to drink with him. I recommended the unemployed Stevens – who was, however, still in bed. Hamilton now decided to go and wake him as he had questions to ask about the investment in Tel-Hotel which he had made on his own behalf, and Hamish's, in Venice. Benj Crud came up to suggest a walk in the woods, but him I repelled by jamming my face into *Clarissa* and ignoring him. Philippa pranced along to say that she would like to be massaged and would return the service. Surely, I remarked, that was

Guy Nevill's duty and privilege? But Guy, it seemed, was away on the sea-marshes, bird-watching. Then she might, I suggested, amuse herself with Adam, who was a wholesome boy and not too fussy about disparities in age. In a tantrum of priggery caused by 'this odious and cynical notion', Philippa departed towards her room where she would, she said spitefully as she retreated, 'lose myself in transcendental meditation of a kind wholly beyond your meagre understanding'. Hamish interrupted her and conscribed her, glad as she was of any male attention, for the weeding which 'some people are too superior to soil their hands with'. Peace at last, I thought: everyone except the absent Guy, who was in any case far too courteous ever to interrupt others engaged according to their choice, had had a go at me and I had now got rid of them all. Since I had endured on the previous day the statutory kiss of welcome from the unsavoury old woman, inaccurately called 'the kyria', who served as maid of all work, all possible sources of interference were now exhausted. I settled to enjoy the villainy of Lovelace ... until sweet sleep, although it was only ten-thirty descended heavily upon me.

I was woken by Adam. There had been a nasty row, he said: I must come at once. The whole thing, he reported, had started with Hamish's trying to enlist him, along with Philippa, for weeding. Since Adam knew that I had done a deal with Hamish for him, paying heavily over the usual sum for his bed and board on condition that he should not be used for menial jobs (it was, after all, his holiday), he had politely refused and gone off to compose a poem in the dining-room, where he had spread out his notes, lexicons and whatever on the commodious table. Hamish, hot with resentment against both Ravens for declining the chores proposed to us, too wilful, as I have explained, to acknowledge our undoubted and dearly bought right of exemption, had crept into the dining-room and deliberately set up a through breeze by opening the door at one end and a wide window at the other: with the result that poor Adam's pathetic papers were taken up in a vortex, whirled through the courtyard and away over the golf course to the sea. Adam, being too modest to rate his poem very highly and too good-natured to make a fuss, least of all with one of his hosts, had taken the thing in good part and slouched off for a drink in the drawing-room; but Hamilton, privy to what had passed, deprecated Hamish's shabby behaviour and, being newly come from Stevens' bedroom where he had received sour news, ingeniously punished Hamish by giving him a gloating account of Martin's default (implausibly blamed by Martin on an unnamed Belgian lawyer) and the consequent and total evaporation of their investment of one thousand pounds in Tel-Hotel. Five hundred pounds meant little to Hamilton but a lot to Hamish, who was not only poor but also avaricious. Desperate at the news of Martin's malversation, further galled by the equable manner in which Adam had sustained the spiteful dissolution of his verses, Hamish now started to scream like a rejected whore at Hamilton and then threw much of the day's lunch at him . . . only to remember, after he had pelted away all of the first course and half of the second, that Lord and Lady Glenconner were coming many miles across the island, by long-standing invitation, to take *déjeuner*, as at his silliest he sometimes called it, at one of the clock.

And what, I now said to Adam, could I conceivably do about any of that?

Firstly, said Adam, I might help calm down Hamish, who was by now hysterical with paranoia; secondly, I might use the knowledge of first aid acquired during my military days to assuage the bleeding of Hamilton, who had had his ear split by a soup ladle; and thirdly, I might give him the money to buy the petrol to drive with Crud to the town of Corfu, where they could buy more provisions which Crud, no mean chef, could cook. Philippa had also offered her services, but she was much given, having written a book on aphrodisiac cuisine, to the use of eccentric ingredients, such as blowflies, vervain, and rabbit's sphincter. Hamilton, sycophantic and indeed grovelling as Hamish where the Glenconners were concerned, had therefore ordered Philippa from the kitchen and was preparing his celebrated jam omelette (with a copious admixture of blood from his wounded ear) to supplement whatever Adam and Benj Crud might procure in the Corfiot markets.

By the time I reached the courtyard, which adjoined both dining-room and kitchen, Hamish had been sent into even wilder realms of derangement by the appearance of slug-a-bed Martin, the self-confessed con-artist; while Philippa was complaining to the winds and the trees that no one would trust her gastrological talent; and Hamilton was dispensing jam and gore in equal quantities into a mess of thirty eggs: three for each of the putative lunchers and all that remained in the house . . . although the Glenconners were not expected for a good hour and would have to be allowed at least fifteen minutes more to drink an aperitif before being led to table.

As Hamish was out of any control except possibly God's, I began by attending to Hamilton's ear. While Benj and Adam juddered off down the drive in the Renault 5 (or 4), I set to with wine vinegar and brown paper, there being little else in the way of curatives available, and eventually stopped the flux, leaving Hamilton in moderate comfort to go on making his huge and apparently futile omelette. Meanwhile Martin had had the presence of mind to lead Philippa away for 'therapy' (God knows what), before she could cast a spell in her fit of malignant frustration on the kitchen and its contents; and I myself, since Hamish was still beyond my comfort or discipline, returned to my point of *bella vista*, to Lovelace and Clarissa. Gradually peace was restored. Whatever 'therapy' Martin had devised for Philippa had evidently worked, as she was now wandering quietly round the garden sucking her thumb. Martin himself came and sat with me, doing silent if obviously troubled calculations in a small, red accounts-book. Hamilton was whisking raw eggs and ichor. Hamish, though still non-negotiable, was no longer screeching his imprecations but mouthing them at Hamilton's back.

Then three things happened. Guy returned from his bird-watching and started, with courteous caresses which would have been refused from any of the rest of us but were acceptable from the heir to a marquessate, to console Hamish. Adam and Benjamin returned from foraging with an assortment of tripes and sausages. And the Glenconners, a good thirty minutes early, sailed up the drive in their oscillating estate waggon and disembarked with well-bred self-effacement, murmuring gently about a cancelled appointment with their lawyer and their wish just to walk in the garden, unattended, until the official time for their arrival. They were out of luck. Hamilton shot out of the kitchen to claim them for his own before anyone else could and led them away, chattering and preening like a parrot, on a tour of the garden accompanied by his own much studied lecture on the house and its history. However, this was just as well as it left the kitchen empty and enabled Guy to lead Hamish, by tactful gradations, up to the pan full of clotted fluid and persuade him that with Hamish's skill, and the savoury visceral colloids purchased by Benj and Adam, an 'amusing' dish could soon be contrived. More therapy: there is nothing like occupation as a balm for disappointed greed and ruptured vanity, and Hamish rapidly became himself again, comforted by the soft words and canny, paddling fingers of the next owner of half the county of Sussex.

As this suspect dish was brewing, Benj and Adam laid my marble table, the afternoon being clement, in the courtyard; while Hamilton, still leading the tour of inspection at a brisk strut but beginning to be bored with his discourse, now hankered to show off more dramatically to the Glenconners by making one or the other of the rest of us look small in front of them. He was badly off target with Philippa, who, accosted *en passant* with a sly sexual insult cleverly disguised as banter, just went drifting on with her thumb still in her mouth. Coming in swift course on Martin and me, Hamilton determined on another attempt: 'Here we have politics and letters sitting together,' he announced to the Glenconners; 'both, as usual, concerning themselves solely with money – handfuls of silver, as Browning has it.'

Martin, of whom this was indeed true, looked up as sharp (for all his puffy cheeks) as a Neapolitan pickpocket and remarked: 'Talking of handfuls of silver, duckie, do you remember that time at school when one of the beaks counted out thirty shilling pieces to you after you'd sneaked about Abingdon's crib of Ovid? You were jealous, I remember, because Abingdon was congratulated on his construe and you'd buggered yours up.'

Christopher Glenconner, immensely decorative and supposedly deaf, began to chuckle and did not stop for the rest of the afternoon. Elizabeth Glenconner, a very kind woman who tried to believe the best of everybody, was divided between distress on my behalf and Martin's at our being so nastily chivvied, and anxiety about the effect on Hamilton of Martin's shrewd riposte. Hamilton capered on, quivering and sniffing for a new victim: my lord and my lady straggled after him, Elizabeth smiling back to show sympathy, not so much with us as with the predicament of the entire human race. Hamilton was headed off by Benj as he sought to enter the kitchen and disrupt Hamish, whereupon he conjectured that his most likely prey was Adam, to whom Benj had been talking about techniques of oil painting – with such effect that Adam was now about to desert poetry forever for the delights of making images and was still dazed by his new dream.

'Tell us about sex at Bedales, Adam,' said Hamilton, eager to dispel the happiness on Adam's face and hoping to embarrass the diffident boy whom he remembered from that Christmas in Venice. But things had moved on with Adam, and although Hamilton's shrill, conceited voice shook him sharply out of his vision of artistry, the word 'sex' moved his spirit to enthuse about another kind of bliss.

'Oh,' said Adam, 'we have daily petting parties in a hay loft. One boy, one girl – but an alarm clock rings every ten minutes for us to change over, so that we don't get bored. The girls all say that I have a very delicate and exciting touch; one of them' – naming the daughter of a famous noble and military family – 'comes like a boy. She actually seems to squirt white stuff.'

Adam, in his delight, had not noticed the Glenconners and had therefore spoken with confidence and brio. Christopher beamed at him while continuing, at the same time, to chuckle over Martin's pleasantry. Elizabeth smiled like Teresa at the attentions of the angel, and said, 'Charming'. Hamilton, who had sought to humiliate four people, had merely succeeded in being ignored by Philippa, put down by Martin, and upstaged by Adam. He was now afflicted with an attack of what Hamish and I used to call his 'nose face', which meant that his rather spatulate nose now flattened itself and seemed to spread right round his cheeks to his ears. He produced a large cigar, failed to light it because it leaked, gestured the Glenconners into chairs in the courtyard, and called on nobody in particular to 'bring Elizabeth and Christopher a drink', a demand which went unanswered as neither the respondent nor the type of drink was specified.

Hamish and Guy, both smiling mysteriously, now appeared from the kitchen carrying between them a vast earthenware terrine. Philippa was called but simply wandered away in another direction (what *had* Martin done to her?); Benj and Adam sat down, by her invitation, on either side of Elizabeth; Martin and myself, having been summoned, sat down on either side of Glenconner by his invitation. Wretched Hamilton, grinding the two halves of his cigar – which he had snapped in petulance – in either fist, stamped up the outside steps to his bedroom, where he flung open the windows directly above us and made loud lamenting noises, which might have been translated by the attentive as 'They all hate me because I'm a Jew', but which in the event went unheeded. Guy and Hamish sat down happily together, and Hamish started to dish out the copious eggs, blood, jam, lights and guts confection, which was judged to be a huge success.

When it was finished, Guy said: 'There was one very special ingredient. Hamish has been rather jumpy this morning, so I persuaded him to soothe himself, as neurotic actors often do before a performance, by ejaculating . . . into the mixture in the bowl.'

'Very nutritious, they say,' said the imperturbable Glenconner.

'An important element in benevolent magic potions,' said Elizabeth.

Hamilton blubbered louder than ever, and even stuck his head out of the window, but was ignored. Philippa still wandered but was not missed. Triumph had been snatched from catastrophe; the afternoon was, after all, proving a fête of wit and jollity.

'What is this?' said Martin, picking an ill-printed magazine from the table.

'It is the latest edition of *Bananas**,' said Elizabeth Glenconner: 'I brought it in case any of you should be interested.'

'Its founder and editor,' explained Hamish to Martin, 'is Elizabeth's daughter, Emma.'

'Emma Tennant?' said Martin; 'Mrs Alexander Cockburn?'

'She's more or less finished with him,' said Christopher, like Yorke and Booker before him. 'She goes through the goodies quite quickly.'

'She's really only interested in her literary career,' said Elizabeth: 'that, and being modern. She's always ticking me off for *not* being modern. The last time was when I referred to some girl as being very plain and her sister as being very beautiful, to make up for it. These days, apparently, you're not allowed to say that people are plain or beautiful. That is to discriminate, Emma says.'

'Well, she certainly hasn't shown much discrimination,' said Martin, who had drunk a great deal of wine, 'about what she's printed in her mag. I've never seen such a load of rubbish. There's something

---

* The second 'a' is apparently short like the other two: *Bănănăs*.

called *Ode to Spring* which is just a jumble of mathematical symbols. Even the bits in English make no sense whatever.'

Glenconner looked uneasy, then looked at Elizabeth, who was clearly upset and angry. There are limits to the tolerance even of those who try to believe the best of everybody, and those limits are usually reached and passed when their offspring is criticised – especially if the criticism is just. But of course Elizabeth was much too well-bred to make a row when she was a guest.

'Perhaps . . . you should read it more carefully,' she said.

'She is at least being consistent,' Martin continued. 'If she won't allow girls to be described as plain or pretty on the grounds, one may suppose, that such talk is "elitist", logically she should not, and clearly she does not, bother herself whether what she publishes in her journal is good or bad. If one throws out standards of physical beauty, one is also bound to throw out standards of aesthetic or literary merit. But one is compelled to wonder a) how she *does* define the difference between ugly girls and comely ones, and b) by what possible criteria she chooses what to publish in *Banānas*.'

'*Banănas*,' insisted Elizabeth. 'I know that Emma does believe in making literary distinctions.' *

'Neither her belief nor her practice are readily discernible in this,' said Martin, making a ball of *Bananas* and shying it under the marble table. 'But I'll happily concede your point rather than give you the lie direct, and omit *Bananas* from our discussion from this time forth and forever more. What I *do* still want to know is how she defines the difference between plain girls and handsome girls . . . or between plain boys and handsome boys, come to that. Or does she not perceive the difference?'

'She's always perceiving it,' said Glenconner; 'why else has she had so many husbands?'

'But she refuses, we are told, to let her mother use "discriminating" epithets. Now, if you perceive or discern that males or females can be attractive or disagreeable or downright repellent to look at – and obviously, as you say, Mrs Cockburn does so perceive or discern – why

*And has since written several distinguished and fascinating novels. SR.

91

not use clear words in the matter? Not when the person in question is present – that would be discourteous – but when talking to others. It seems that Emma forbade her mother to do that: a) Why? and b) what sort of words *was* she meant to use?'

'I suppose I was meant to be charitable,' said Elizabeth humbly, 'and not refer to the matter at all.'

'But that has to be nonsense,' said Martin. 'One has to refer to such things from time to time and one has to be truthful about them. If one is consulted, one has to say that Hamish here is a real dish; that Simon is passable but past it; that Adam is lumpy but young and wholesome; that Philippa – where the hell is she? – is a long, beaky streak; that Hamilton is quite fetching in a whiny Wailing Wall sort of way; that Benj Crud is a sly-looking, paranoiac, and predatory Jew, *par excellence* a *jewy* kind of Jew — '

' — I think,' said Elizabeth, 'that we ought to be going, Christopher. I am not at all happy about — '

' — Don't worry about me,' said Benj Crud. 'Martin and I are old friends. I'm used to this sort of thing when he's drunk.'

'I was not worrying about you,' said Elizabeth sorrowfully. 'I'm afraid that Christopher and I have somehow upset Hamilton. I think I must go upstairs and say a word or two. If we are in the process of leaving, that will seem quite natural.'

'I shouldn't bother,' said Hamish, 'it's good for him not to get attention.'

'He's been very quiet for the last few minutes,' said Adam, looking up at Hamilton's window.

'Not any longer,' quacked Hamilton, his head whisking out of the window like Mr Punch's. 'This is my house, and I *command* you *all* to go away *now*. Christopher and Elizabeth can go back to their own home, and the rest of you can go to the Hotel Cavaliere or wherever you bloody well like. If no one is going to take any notice of me, I might just as well be here alone.'

'But,' said Elizabeth, 'I was just coming up to you.'

'I can do without *your* patronage,' said Hamilton, 'or anyone else's. I am, after all, a *Sephardic* Jew, and I don't have to put up with the airs and graces of the second wife of a second baron whose father was in trade.'

'Leave her to me,' said Hamish: 'I'll go up and deal with *her* tantrums.'

Up he went. Silence upstairs. We spoke in hushed voices.

'The trouble is,' Guy told us, 'that on the morning when they were meant to go before the local archon earlier this week, to register the house, Hamilton had such a hangover that Hamish had to go alone. He said that he and Hamilton owned the house fifty-fifty*, and so it has been recorded. Irrevocably recorded. So Hamilton is sulking because he says that Hamish has stolen half of the house that has been paid for with his money.'

'No, no,' said Hamish, who had come back down the steps while Guy was talking. 'It's all far less dramatic than that. More squalid but less dramatic.' He showed us an ashtray he was carrying; the cigarette ends seemed curiously animated. 'I warned her,' said Hamish; 'I warned her against eating pork when we were in Morocco last month. "It isn't kosher," I said, "and the Moslems don't approve either. It is suspect flesh, and what is more they undercook it." But *she* had to know better. Roast pork, so called, she would have. "Very well," I said, "don't blame me if you get food poisoning – or worms." And now' – he brandished the ashtray with its writhing contents – 'worms is just what she's got. No one need move. Just sit tight while I take her into the town, where darling Doctor Asclepiades will give her a powerful enema and keep her in his nursing home to make sure it does the trick. Then we can all have a peaceful dinner, for once, without her showing off like the Queen of Sheba.'

'Please come quickly, somebody,' called Philippa from the garden. 'I've just drunk my Floris Stephanotis bath essence. I wasn't really concentrating, and I thought it was one of the miniature vodkas I always travel with . . .'

Happy, happy days at Opsiopoulos in the Seventies . . . all, alas, ended when Hamish and Hamilton parted at the end of the decade and sold the house off to provide Hamish's alimony.

---

*There would also have been a legal necessity, at that time, to nominate a Greek as formal head of the syndicate which owned the house, since Corfu was technically a 'border' area. That does not affect this anecdote, however; though one may reflect that H and H were lucky their nominee was honest, as many such used their legal standing to assist them in various types of fraud or malversation – a Greek speciality.

iii) The Morea

I have remarked already that I was, at the period of the Glenconner luncheon, 'mildly' infatuated with Hamish. I have never quite known why. Physically he was no great catch, for while he had a handsome enough face and a well-found torso, his thighs were mean and his calves spindly – as Hamilton often used to observe when he wished to annoy him, adding that a good stint of National Service, for which he had been five years too young, might have remedied these faults and those of his character as well. The latter included conceit of his carnal attractions and intellectual attainments (mediocre); greed for flattery; covert resentment and unremitting adulation of the rich; spiteful rejection of failed or fallen friends, unless kudos was to be had, in carefully selected cases, by appearing to succour them; murderous jealousy of sexual, social, or artistic success; profligacy with Hamilton's money when Hamilton had it and extortion when he hadn't; treachery and falsehood; and the conviction that his judgements in all spheres were infallible. On the other hand, there were a few things to be said for his credit – a nice turn of phrase; his affable company during journeys or parties of pleasure, provided always that he was having absolutely his own way; his subtle talents as a chef – but not nearly enough to account for my infatuation once the debit column has been summed. How, then – *come, Muse, and tell* – did this infatuation first get a grip on me? A kindly touch early on, a pretty, passing caress of Cupid (as in the beginning I told myself it was), but cruel and enduring as the months passed, and then the seasons, and then the years.

It all started – *come, Muse, and sing a song of love in idleness* – in the

Morea, more usually called the Peloponnese, a year or so before the gathering at Opsiopoulos which I have just described. In the autumn of 1971 Hamilton had been summoned back from his holiday in Corcyra a fortnight before his time; and Hamish, who was sick of housekeeping, proposed to me and his friend Alexis (one of Hamish's many heterosexual admirers) that we should leave Opsiopoulos and the Island of the Phaeacians and 'go on a tripette'.

So on a tripette we went. *Come, baneful Muse, and tell your tale of folly.* First we drove to Athens, and after paying swift duty to the Acropolis and the National Museum, we set off for Delphi, which Hamish was too restless to pause and inspect, being by now, like the nobleman in Lucretius' his poem, obsessed with movement for movement's sake, thinking thus to outrun boredom and even Death. We crossed the Gulf of Corinth on a car ferry, turned east for Nauplion, were allowed by Hamish to spend half an hour en route at Tiryns but not to make the brief diversions necessary to visit Mycenae or Epidauros and, after a night at Nauplion, headed over the mountains for Black Sparta. Here Hamish became easier, for whatever reason, and let us pause to consider our journey and its stages with some care.

It was eventually decided that we should spend the coming night in Sparta, a dull rectangular conurbation, marvellously sited, however, almost at the foot of the range of Taygetus or Taïygetos and having a passable, Class A, Xenia. The next morning there would be a visit to the museum and the faintly rude Roman mosaics, then to the modest and even furtive remains of Lakedaimon, ancient Sparta.

From Lakedaimon we would proceed west to Mistra (*Come, Muse, to wake the first sweet memories of desire*), where we would patronise the spectacular assembly of Byzantine churches and despots' palaces, which climb the long, steep slope towards the Frankish castle of William de Villehardouin, the crown of the city but not of the mountain; for this surges far and high, ever farther and higher, to the summit of Taïygetos, range of Artemis the Huntress of the Peak – its lower regions having been much favoured, once upon a time, for the disposal of unwanted Spartan infants, the maimed and the female. The road across this range we would follow, over the ridge, down through the Vale of Messene and on to Kalamata by the shore of the Messenian Gulf, then famous for its fish, which these days would probably poison you on sight. Then we would motor west, across the westernmost prong at the bottom of the Morea, to Navarino, otherwise Homer's Sandy Pylos – more or less; we would see old Nestor's Palace just across the bay, and spend the night at the xenia – regrettably only Class Gamma or C – that had been named for him. The next day it would be heigh boys for the North; for Elis of the Pines; for the temple of Bassai; and Olympia of the runners, the wrestlers and the long-maned horses; then into Arcadia, which was once frequented, so the poet said, not only by nymphs and their shepherds, but also by Death. For it was He who had announced, '*Atque ego in Arcadia sum*' – 'I, too, am in Arcadia.'

Our progress went much in the manner proposed until we were walking up the hill at Mistra. I was grinding on about Gemistos Plethon, the Platonist, who had lived there for much of the first half of the fifteenth century.

'So famous were his lectures,' I pontificated, 'that in 1423 they were attended by the learned Grecian, Bessarion, who was particularly impressed by — '

' — What is a Grecian, please?' said peaches-and-cream, but utterly masculine, Alexis.

'A Scholar of Greek,' I said grandly.

'Talking of Scholars of Greek,' said Hamish, 'do I not remember that your chum Paddy Leigh Fermor lives not far from here?'

'He is an acquaintance, alas, rather than a chum,' I said. 'About ten years ago I was invited with a party to a castle he was living in near Rome. A few months later Burgo Partridge and I had lunch with him in London before we went to Crete in 1959. He seemed to think we should enjoy tramping round the island with knapsacks and gave us a letter of introduction, in fluent and stylish modern Greek, to all the experts on sleeping in caves, and the concomitant horrors, whom he'd known during the war.'

'If you went to his castle *and* had lunch with him in London, you must know him well enough to call on him now. In fact it would be very impolite of you *not* to call on him now.'

'I haven't seen him for more than a decade. He lives a long distance down the Mani. Right out of our way.'

'If you telephone him,' persisted Hamish, 'he might invite us for the night. We could simply turn left for the Mani in Kalamata, instead of right for Pylos, and get there well before dark.'

I began to spell it all out. Paddy Leigh Fermor, I said, lived at Kardomili which, though admittedly less than half-way down the coast of the Mani, was only to be reached by a winding and treacherous road. If, therefore, Paddy did not ask us to stay the night, we should have a weary and perilous drive in the pitch dark, back up the Mani and then west to Navarino/Pylos – where we would almost certainly arrive too late for dinner. Since Paddy's house at Kardomili was still building, I went on, it would be difficult for him to lodge us, even if he wanted to, and why should he? The chances of our having to make a nasty, noctivagant course of some fifty miles from Kardomili to Navarino were therefore heavily odds on. These objections were compounded, I perorated, by my not knowing Paddy's telephone number, if indeed he was so ill-advised as to have a telephone, and by our being unable, therefore, to do him the courtesy of asking his permission before obtruding ourselves upon his peace.

But Hamish was implacable. *Come, Muse, and chant a lay of Ātē, the dark goddess, who makes crooked the will of man.* As an habitual and hardened tuft-hunter, he had scented the propinquity of a rare and delectable tuft. For a start, he said, however disagreeable the driving, he himself would be doing it. He had heard, 'from somebody who knew the area', that the roads were now much improved (with an eye to vamping the amenities for vulgar tourism) as far down the Mani as Areopolis, and Kardomili was indisputably this side of that. Grecians and Philhellenes were renowned, he pursued, for their ample hospitality, however suddenly it might be required of them and however limited the space at their disposal, and the last thing they desired or expected was to be warned by telephone.

'So there, Simon, is an answer to all your objections.'

'Except in this respect – that such an incursion would be a hideous breach of good manners.'

'Of conventional good manners, perhaps. But men like Leigh Fermor have little time for hypocritical conventions. If you have been as intimate with him as you claim – '

' — I never claimed intimacy with him.'

'If you have been in his company as often as you have told us, it is

99

your duty, now that you are passing so close to him in a strange country, to seek him out.'

'The country is not strange to him,' I said. 'He requires no news of England, no attention from marauding Englishmen. He came here specifically to avoid such ghastly disruptions.'

But Hamish was adamant. When we had driven over Taïygetos and come, at about tea-time, to Kalamata, he simply set his wilful face and took the turning to the Mani and Kardomili. Sweet, drowsy Alexis, who was so vague that he never knew where he was and so laid back that he didn't in the least care where he was going, appeared hardly to notice. As for myself, I knew that Hamish, when in a fit of snobbery, was impossible to deter. He had made up his mind that he was going to add Leigh Fermor to his frame of reference and tittle-tattle, and there was an end of it. We drove in silence under the Castle of Zarnaba, round and round the coastal hills as the evening crept over them, slowly making ground to the South.

At the southern tip of the Mani lies Cape Tainaros or Taenarum (Matapan); one entrance, so they say, to the world of the shadows of the dead. Devoutly I wished that that was our destination, that we could just go bumping through Kardomili without a pause, pass Areopolis and brave the road, no doubt even viler than this one, to the gates of Black Death – anything rather than disturb poor Paddy on the strength of my two or three brief meetings with him and a tenuous correspondence. But there was no escape. Hamish, like the hound of heaven, would hunt down Leigh Fermor, dragging the heedless Alexis – one more face to be fed, one more body to accommodate – and my own dismally embarrassed self behind him.

By now, as Homer has it, all the ways were dark. 'This is Kardomili,' murmured Hamish as we rattled into a benighted village that was unlit, unsigned, unnamed, indistinguishable from a dozen such through which we had passed. Hamish was, of course, right. He then discovered the only human being who was abroad in the whole peninsula, uttered a few words in formal but very clear Greek, and received back a low, demotic volley. He had a talent for languages and could have made a fortune in tips as doorkeeper to Babel.

'Paddy's house' – 'Paddy' already? – 'is half a mile further on,' he now told us, 'and one third of a mile out of the village. The house itself is almost on the sea, a furlong from the road. There is no drive, but there is a narrow path, which leads from the first bend beyond the village, over a kind of heath, to some half-finished steps which mount to a terrace.'

And so it was. Hamish parked tidily and safely beyond the bend and well off the track. He examined the stone wall to the right of the track; showed us where to climb over it; found the narrow path – about six inches narrow – led us along it with the accuracy and brio of Sir John Moore leading the Light Division; anticipated the stone steps; halted the party under his command; called me forward from the rear; propelled me up the brief flight, ahead of himself and Alexis, on to the terrace.

'Now do your stuff with Paddy,' he said. 'Paddy' again.

All this time I had been judging Paddy, as I tended to judge everybody in those days, by myself. He would receive us with bare civility, I thought; offer us a drink in a tone which, like the Latin particle *num*, expected or certainly hoped for the answer 'No'; demonstrate with a gesture that he was still 'only camping' in the place himself, and helpfully opine that the hours of dinner in the distant Greek hostelries available to us were generous (as well they might be, since all food in Greek restaurants has been suppurating in lukewarm cauldrons for days or even weeks), but not sempiternal. Some such sequence of muted greeting, specious denial of resources, and smooth but swift dismissal – the swifter the better, thought I, for then there would be less time during which I must endure the shame that was already flooding my thighs and lower buttocks with crural sweat – some such formula of reluctant hail and brisk farewell I was now expecting.

The event was very different. As we walked uncertainly along the terrace, which was lit only by a storm lantern hissing on a low table, Paddy came nervously out of the house by a door at the far end, looked at us with puzzlement rather than resentment, and said: 'Simon. How nice to see you after all this time. These are your friends?'

He shook hands with me, then with Hamish and Alexis – who had, of course, no idea whatever of who or what he was; he settled us all on crude but comfortable chairs, which were ranged against the wall, did not ask us what we would like to drink but fetched retsina in a two-handed clutch of half-litre taverna pannikins, saying 'No proper jugs yet', poured for all, and raised his tumbler.

'Χαίρετε,' he said: 'be welcome to my house.'

He then told us of the Mani; its history of feuds and famines; of the pirates who had infested its coast through the centuries; of the indifference of Byzantine emperors towards the place and its people, and the love of the harsh hills borne by the Greek King Otho, who built a modest villa by the harbour of Limenaion, just north of Areopolis. He told us a legend of Cape Tainaros, one of which I had never heard, which asserts that the dead emerge from the cave there on the last night of every thousand years and fly across the sea to Cytherea, the island of Aphrodite, where they are granted real bodies with which to make love to whomsoever they choose for the single hour between eleven pm and midnight, after which they immediately revert to being shadows and return to their accustomed domicile as the last stroke of twelve ushers in the New Year, the New Century, the New Millennium.

'Of course,' Paddy expounded, 'the first time this rare anniversary occurred in the Christian Era was the year 1000 AD. The Christians of Cytherea, who knew of the legend from pagan record, were in a terrible taking lest they be seduced or raped by these spirits made flesh – presumably by the enchantment of Aphrodite and not by the authority of the church – and locked and triple-barred themselves into their houses, stopping up all apertures with boards secured by clay. The next day, the Bishop of Cytherea, who had heroically remained outside armed with Cross and crozier in order to exorcise any ghosts that might appear before they changed from larval to carnal and were capable of lustful outrage – the Bishop, I say, reported that no revenants at all had turned up; and it was therefore assumed that Aphrodite had lost her powers since the accession of Christ the King and that there would be no further infernal and amorous invaders – who were not, in any case, due to come again for another thousand years. Next New Year's Eve, therefore, they all carried on in their usual fashion with religious and vinous excess – only to be caught unawares and molested in multitudes by swarms of horny cadavers, who had relations, as the journalists say, with just about every human being on the island between eleven of the clock and the Cinderella hour. What had gone wrong was that the Cythereans had made the stupid and vulgar error of thinking that the new millennium started and the old ended at the beginning of 1000; whereas, of course, they only start and end with the arrival of 1001, when the year 1000, the last of the old millennium, is finally seen out. So the Cythereans had shut themselves up like nuns a year too early and were wandering about in the open, totally vulnerable, when the crunch came. One sometimes wonders whether the archon (Mayor) or whoever had not purposely misled them.

'In any event, followed the most horrible trouble of every kind. What was to be done about women who had been impregnated by the visitants? Or about the babies they would bear nine months later? The dead, it appears, do not bother with condoms or *coitus interruptus* on the millennial spree. To make things worse, there was a lot of mischief from old men and women. These, having not had any sexual entertainment for many years, had been accosted by the undead, who had too little time to discriminate, and reawakened by their enthusiastic attentions. So the old now gave great offence by copulating openly with their coevals (being thoroughly overexcited by the discovery that they were up to it after all, and being in any case too old to care about appearances) and, even worse, by importuning their far more appetising juniors – who were hard put to it to fend the old pests off . . . or, in some cases, developed gerontophiliac tastes and techniques which inflamed the already sizzling scandal.

'As the Greeks are notorious for never learning from their own history,' Paddy pursued, 'for look how they persist in selling their few remaining trees, despite the desolation thus created by their feckless forefathers, it is to be feared that the inhabitants of Cytherea will fall into precisely the same error at the onset of the years 2000 and 2001, taking precautions on the former occasion and exposing themselves on the latter. Though of course they may just get the dates right this time, as the affair will probably, *pace* the Church, be hyped as a tourist attraction.'

Of this and other matters Paddy discoursed, beguiling us as we sat and drank lime-like retsina on his terrace in the moonless and starless night. After passing from the tale of the tumescent Tainarians, he gave some account of other entrances to the underworld, most notably that at the sanctuary of Persephone at Ephyra, with its brilliantly equipped Necromanteion and splendid view of the Acherousian Lake; and then remarked, 'I fear lest it grows late. I have but two slices of bread, and one and a half unattractive fishes. Even if one among us had miraculous powers, we would hardly wish the amount of such fare increased. But young men like you surely have sleeping bags or comparable equipment. If you wish, you may sleep on this terrace, "under the wide and starry sky". Correction: no stars. Perhaps they will emerge later.'

'I think,' said Alexis, who occasionally showed unsuspected awareness, 'that we had best be on the road. Goodnight, sir, and thank you for your marvellous stories.'

'I shall see you along the path,' said Paddy: 'possibly you are prudent: there will be no breakfast either.'

As we trailed along in Indian file, Paddy laughed gleefully and said, ' "The night is hellish dark", to quote a character from *Mister Sponge's Sporting Tour*, but does not, alas, "smell of cheese" for our dinner, as it did in Surtees. Does anyone read Surtees now?'

'I do,' said Alexis, 'he makes me laugh.'

Hamish and I were so amazed by the intelligence that Alexis had read anything that we were stunned into silence.

When Alexis evinced no further information or lit. crit., Paddy said, 'I remember Maurice Bowra's saying that the young should be encouraged to read Surtees in place of George Eliot: Surtees would teach them about the callous, bilking, squalid nature of man as it really was, whereas George Eliot gave out an unhealthy air of moral aspiration.'

'Poor Maurice,' I said: 'now that he's had that stroke, he'd be better dead.'

'Whatever do you mean?' said Paddy. 'Better dead? Maurice would never wish that. There never was a man more full of life.'

'What sort of life can he possibly have now?' I said. 'From the learned and witty Warden of Wadham he has declined into a state of geriatric ghastliness. Surely better dead.'

'I don't think Maurice would thank you for saying so,' Paddy said. He was always a "*dum spiro, spero*" man. "While there's life, there's hope." If you went to prison, the first thing you'd know was that Maurice was there passing fivers through the bars to rehabilitate you after your release.'

'But according to Alan Pryce-Jones,' I said – an odious piece of name-dropping – 'when you *were* released and rehabilitated, you'd better not be too happy or successful if you wished to stay in Maurice's good books. He was kindness itself to failure, implacably resentful of success. When an old friend of his was knighted, Maurice interrupted the bearer of the news with a great bellow of "Stop. *Stop*. I cannot bear THE PAIN."'

'What has this to do with Maurice's illness?' said Paddy coolly.

'Simply this: he was a great one for bringing comfort to others on their deathbeds, but was not too liberal with his congratulations if they recovered – and certainly not if they wrote a distinguished and best-selling book of their thoughts while in the valley of the shadow and married a beautiful heiress on the strength of it. This raises some interesting questions about his attitude to himself now that he is dying – or at least in serious decline. If the survival and triumph of others is so irritating to him, he must realise, as a man of sense and intellect, that his own recovery might cause grave displeasure among his acquaintance.'

'Yes, he might realise that,' conceded Paddy, 'and make a magnificent Bowra joke about it.'

Conscious that I was perversely indulging in malice and even in malignance – probably, to be fair, because of my empty stomach – I nevertheless went banging on.

'Alan Pryce-Jones says', I said as we reached the road and our car, 'that in Bowra's bottom drawer there are a whole lot of embarrassing sub-Housmanesque verses about boys and what he calls striplings. Pity the literary executor, Alan says, having to sort that lot out.'

'I'd give anything to be Maurice's literary executor,' Paddy said. 'I know those critical books are pretty damn boring, but think of all those gorgeous parodies. Lots of them have been shown to nobody at all, you know, and if those are up to the standard of the ones we have read – what a Lucullan banquet! There's that heavenly one of Hardy's verses about the sudden death of his first wife, in *Poems 1912-13*.

'O how you went so fast,
Without any palaver:
I found when I spent at last
It was all over your cadaver.'

'Marvellous stuff,' concluded Paddy. 'One hopes there are many more like that still to be sifted.'

'What a splendid fellow,' said Alexis, as we drove north through Kardomili for Kalamata and Pylos.

'You were pretty sour just at the end,' said Hamish to me.

'I'm sorry my behaviour didn't meet with your approval. I thought that you were getting rather restless – no doubt because you weren't the centre of attention.'

'Girls, girls, girls,' said the peacemaker Alexis.

Although it seemed like the middle of the night when we arrived in Pylos/Navarino, it was not much past nine. But the Nestor was full. We drove down to the southern end of the bay, to the Castello. By this time a gibbous moon had sidled through the clouds; one could see an amusing 'Hammer Productions' castle on the slope above the hotel, and there was a notice outside announcing that dinner was served until ten o'clock and that Diners' Club cards were accepted. Spirits rose. Spirits rose still further when we inspected our rooms, all of which had 'magic casements, opening on the foam' of the Bay of Navarino. Spirits fell again when the foam immediately began to stink of human and industrial excreta, and when it became abundantly apparent that the beds were damp.

'Leigh Fermor wouldn't mind a little thing like that,' I said despondently; 'he'd have his sleeping bag anyway.'

'He'd despise the lot of us,' said Alexis, 'as silly little cissies whining about a spot of wet on the bed.'

'Mine is like a swamp,' said Hamish; 'and there are *animiculae* in it.'

'Serves you right,' I sniffed. 'If you hadn't made us go all the way down to Kardomili, we'd have arrived here in time to get into the Nestor.'

'How do you know the beds aren't damp in the Nestor?'

'Because the Nestor's a government xenia, and everything is properly done in such places.'

'The last time I stayed in a xenia,' said Alexis, 'that very grand one in the citadel of Arta, I found a used Tampax on the top of the wardrobe.'

'What were you doing, looking at the top of the wardrobe?'

'I was depositing a used French letter, as there was no wastepaper basket. Come along, chums: dinner.'

There was none at the Castello. We pointed at the notice. The manager, who had two days' growth of diseased fungus on his chin, shrugged and pouted in imbecile peasant fashion and pointed back up the bay towards the Nestor. Dinner was just over at the Nestor; but they could give us fruit and feta, the goat cheese which in those days made one's teeth squeal. We were directed to a restaurant in the square by the harbour. It was called the Clytemnestra, turned out to be Class Theta, and offered two pots of pasta so pale and swollen with lying in bilge water that one was put in mind of Mrs Hardy's corpse in Bowra's parody. We went back to the Nestor. It was locked. We banged on the door. The waiter stuck his head out of an upper window and said he hoped we had dined well at the Clytemnestra.

'As you know,' said Hamish as we trudged by the scummy waters to the Castello, 'a lot of what Leigh Fermor was telling us came straight out of his book on the Mani. He might have been reciting a prepared piece.'

'The story of the randy spooks of Tainaros wasn't in his book on the Mani,' I said.

'That was a special treat,' said Hamish, 'to make up for the lack of food. I wonder if he was lying about that?'

'I shouldn't blame him if he was. I told you we shouldn't just barge in on him like that.'

'He couldn't have thought much of you,' said Hamish, 'to turn you and your friends away hungry. You know, I think he must have got your number all those years ago when you and Burgo Partridge were having lunch with him and he was telling you what a wonderful time you could have sleeping out in Crete. I bet you put on that snooty, fruity look of yours, as if to say, "Catch me sleeping out with a load of smelly Cretans." I bet you did, and he noticed, and he thought, "Raven is a snobby soppy CUNT if ever I saw one", and that's why he couldn't be bothered to feed us.'

And so to Acherusian bed.

The Castello did not accept my Diners' card in settlement of the bill. When we pointed to the DINERS' sign, the manager prised some filth out of his fungus, rolled it into a ball, and made an obscene gesture with it.

Nestor's palace at ancient Pylos was the most boring thing out: just a plan made with stones in the turf.

'This must have been where Telemachos slept,' I said, trying to make the show go with a bit of a swing, 'on the porch. Listening to the waves from the many-sounding sea.'

'I expect he just had a wank,' said Hamish, 'all over those purple coverlets which Homer is always going on about.'

'Like what happened to Mrs Hardy,' said Alexis.

Her fate seemed to have caught everyone's imagination.

'I've never known worse value for ten drachmae,' said Hamish as we drove on towards the town of Khora, where there was a museum devoted to finds on the site of the palace: 'I vote we give the museum a miss.'

'No,' said Alexis firmly: 'we said we'd go there, and we must stick to our plan.'

Oh, Alexis. His insistence made one happy day and thirteen dismal years.

In the museum at Khora were swords and cups, palatial pottery and fragments of fresco which made one understand what an exciting and seductive place Nestor's palace would have been to live in; with its long view of the sea and the curving beach, on to which, before the time of the classical harbour, brilliant and distinguished guests would disembark, pulling their ship up over the whistling sand, to be feasted and filled with wine, there and then on the beach itself as like as not. After which they would sing, on request, for their supper, telling their tall tales of Troy and Crete, and Aulis and old Nile. The jewels and wine-jars in the little museum conjured such a scene for us, there among the grimy glass cases and the hawking curators; and suddenly Hamish said what Nestor had once said as he handed the cup to a newly come guest.

' "Εὔχεονῦν, ὦ ζεῖνε . . . Pray now, stranger, to the Lord Poseidon, for his is the feast whereon you have chanced in coming hither . . . δὸς καὶ τού τῷ ἔπειτα . . . then give thy friend also the cup, the cup of honey-sweet wine." ' He mimed the passing of a wine-cup from himself to me.

Whereupon ἄτη (ātē), Infatuation, bane of mortal man, sent for his affliction by the gods that are forever, entered my soul and set me to loving Hamish. I owe Alexis no thanks, after all, for bringing us into the museum that morning. *Say, Muse, what manner of man was my beloved*: a more lethal object of love, or even affection, than Hamish would be impossible to conceive.

However this was not, for the time being, apparent. The next few hours passed in a light, bright air of enchantment, as we drove up what was little better than a goat-path from the coast through Phigaleia – an appropriate place, as the ancient inhabitants and, for all I know, the modern, have a reputation for witchcraft – and on to the temple of Bassai, which Pausanias tells us was built in gratitude to Apollo for lifting a local plague.

He did not lift my plague.

A lunch of no character, food in any case now a matter of indifference, at Andritseina in an unremarkable xenia; then on to Karyteina, where is the thirteenth-century castle, with its faery turrets, of the Lord Geoffery de Bruyère, 'the best knight in all Romany', as Alfred Duggan tells us; the very pattern of Morean chivalry, a glutton for intrigue and adultery. We missed the way to Olympia as evening fell; but what cared I for that, so long as I was being driven by my own knight of the Morea, ever potent in my besotted eyes against dragons and the dark? In any event, we very soon found the road again and by six of the clock were entering the marble halls of the Old Railway Hotel (SPAP), where wispy, Jamesian ladies and gentlemen sat on wicker chairs and quizzed the trio of Hamish the demigod, Alexis the smiling faun, and their attendant and gawping pantaloon.

'Not a woman was allowed in the place,' I said to Alexis and Hamish the next morning as we walked round the gymnasia and temples of Olympia. 'No women, tradesmen, aliens or slaves were allowed inside the sacred precinct. The brothels and the eating-places and all the fun of the great fair were to be found over there, west of the river.'

'The Games were only for men?' said Alexis.

'Only for gentlemen. For a start, only gentlemen could afford to come here. It was a long and expensive journey from most parts of Greece. True, some cities subsidised competitors. But since no one except gentlemen would have been trained, no one except gentlemen received subsidies.'

'Some one once told me,' said Hamish, 'that they had mule cart races here. Not a very gentlemanly sport.'

'They didn't last long. They were considered to have neither antiquity nor dignity in their favour.'

'I see,' said Hamish. 'Pindar would not have approved. It was Pindar who wrote odes in honour of the winners?'

'Yes,' I said, much fancying my pithy style of calling up the past in front of two such, as I then supposed, sympathetic listeners. 'Odes which he was paid very handsomely to compose by posh families, when little Dio or little Telly had just won the junior wrestling, or by municipal sponsors who had, say, entered a chariot. The odes were commissioned on the understanding that they would contain much praise of the families or townships that were paying for them. In theory such praise was confined to legendary ancestors and aboriginal founders, but Pindar was not above accepting an extra twenty per cent to pop in a complimentary couplet about little Dio's daddy or some of the contemporary town councillors.'

'So Pindar,' said Alexis, 'was a sucker-up?'

'An arse-licker,' Hamish said.

'Also a remarkable poet,' I urged.

In silence we surveyed the massive platform on which stood – or rather sprawled – the Temple of Zeus, then walked along the remains of a colonnade to the western end of the stadium. It was a dank, ungracious day. The Pines of Elis on the hill above the precinct clothed the summit like a cowl; the pines in the precinct itself, black, sullen and absolutely still, dripped steadily. Not a day for love; a day for nagging or disillusion. I was only twenty-four hours gone in my folly, so of course nothing could disillusion me, yet; but even so, early ugly doubts could start squirming into the mind, if not the heart.

'Any competitor who cheated or took bribes could be publicly flogged,' I said, as we gazed at the dreary length of the stadium.

'What a pity,' said Alexis, 'that this regulation has been discarded from the modern Olympics.'

'Amateurs and gentlemen could be whipped in public?' said Hamish.

'Only if they disgraced their gentility.'

'Shall we go?'

'Why? There's no hurry,' said Alexis.

'I'm sick of all this rotting rubbish,' Hamish said. 'Greek Antiquity. "An old bitch gone in the teeth," Ezra Pound called it: "a few hundred battered statues". I'm sick of the reverence we are expected to lavish on it, just because it is old. Why can't we pay more attention to modern Greece, to modern problems in this country, modern pastimes? Living people, warm blood, quivering flesh? Here's Simon, spends half an hour a day, as he claims, reading Homer or Plato in the original — '

' — With the help of a crib,' I interposed, trying to draw off this bile, to soothe this facile protest that had come without warning or provocation.

'But you can't speak a word of the demotic, you never try. You make no effort at all to understand modern Greeks or what they say, or even what they write.'

'It's a matter of personal preference,' I said. 'I enjoy archaic and classical Greek literature – and *some* modern Greek literature: Cavafis, Kazantzakis — '

' — Only because Cavafis and Kazantzakis write about the same things, gods and goddesses and pretty little boys romping about,' – he gestured at the stadium – 'the same things as all that classical crew. You don't give a damn for modern Greek political ideals or economics or social ethics — '

' — I like the classics,' I said, 'both Greek and Latin, because they are about the excitement, the charm and the transience of physical pleasure, and about the operations of time, chance and death. These are the great human themes. Why should I bother with the greed and trickery of modern Greek politicians and the squalid whores whom they take as their mistresses? If I want to read about that kind of thing, the classical authors have done it with ten times the style and wit of your demotic tabloids.'

'But the classical authors write – wrote – about the dead.'

'And where's the odds in that? The trashy lot now in power in Athens will be dead soon enough.'

'They are alive *now*. Their ideas and aspirations affect those that live here and now.'

'They don't affect me,' said Alexis. 'I never listen to any politicians, least of all the shower of shit here in the Balkans. They desire power, and must therefore be contemptible as men. I value only independence.'

'And what happens,' I said, 'when the politicians' hankering for power interferes with your taste for independence?'

'Luckily we're English,' said Alexis. 'In England politicians aren't allowed to interfere with people's independence. Or not so's you'd notice.'

'Just you wait a while,' said Hamish. 'Until you get rich.'

'I shall never be rich,' said Alexis. 'I only want enough money to spend from day to day in minding my own business and amusements.'

'They'll get round to you in time,' said Hamish. 'You are – or soon will be if present trends continue – what Orwell's socialists in *Nineteen Eighty-Four* called a "thought criminal". Somebody who despises current political fads, even though he may keep quiet about it for the sake of peace. They're going to hate you worse than they hate anybody.'

'Because they can't touch him,' I said. 'Or not in England.'

'Not yet,' said Hamish. 'I dare say they're working on it.'

I was so much in agreement with his last two or three remarks that I forgot, for that day and many days, that this discussion had started with Hamish's petty and contrived complaints about the classical Greek past and those that love and study it.

PART FOUR

The Black Nile,
with Serpents

i) Grass snakes

'The Beaujolais,' said Suki despondently, 'costs twenty-two pounds a bottle.'

Quite a lot of money in 1963. But we were buying the wine at the Hotel Gordon Pasha in Khartoum, where the Moslem superstition, though not so flagrant as it was later to become, was even then offensively prevalent.

'There'll be nothing at all at Wigi Zigi,' I said: 'we'd better take this. Half and half?'

'No,' said Suki gallantly: 'BIF can pay.'

So I wrapped the bottle in my pyjamas and stuffed it into the grip which I carried with me in the aeroplane to Wigi Zigi, where we arrived in time for tea.

The point about Wigi Zigi was that it was a convenient oasis, with a passable Travelodge, from which to cross the border into Egypt and motor a few miles further along a desert track to Abu Simbel – the old Abu Simbel, when it was still in its proper place, i.e. that in which it had been built. Wigi Zigi had the advantage of being in the Sudan which at that time, on account of some temporary political fashion, was friendly to Great Britain; whereas the Egyptians were being even more than usually stroppy. So although the Egyptians would just allow one to spend a few hours looking at Abu Simbel without being too annoying, it would cost an eye and an ear and a month's fucking about to procure a visa actually to stay in their horrible country. One stayed, then, on Sudanese territory and crossed the border, bribing the officials, in order to visit Abu Simbel where yet more bribes would be exacted from BIF.

Suki was leading publicity lady to BIF (British Imperial Flights). But *can* it have been 'Imperial' as late as 1963, rather than 'International' or 'Intercontinental'? Memory certainly says 'Imperial', and in any case the whole affair has now gone so totally phut that there is no way of checking. Suki, I say, was head publicity lady to this louche and improbable concern and I, as her friend, was enjoying a freebie on a trial BIF trip to Khartoum – with which we were now, thank God, finished – to Wigi Zigi to Abu Simbel, back to Wigi Zigi and on to Beirut – which had not yet been vandalised by the Jews and the Arabs.

The only trouble about Abu Simbel was that in those days everyone insisted that one must see it precisely at dawn, when the newly risen sun shone straight into it and it made (or am I imagining this?) peculiar noises to welcome the new day.

'I've got to share a room with Coral,' [her under-strapper], said Suki. 'Coral says she won't mind if you sleep in there with me . . . though I must say the beds are very close together.'

'Would Coral care to join in, then?'

'You are disgusting, vile, nauseating,' said Suki, grinning and hissing like an Egyptian cat. 'We must all get up for brekky at two-thirty a.m. and then drive to Abu Simbel. You and I, and Coral, are to go in the same taxi. I'll make sure we have it to ourselves. Everyone else on this trip is too hateful even to contemplate.'

'What about Copperlight of the *Manchester Guardian*? He was at King's with me. He was once sick in the bath of the Visitor's Chambers on a night when the Visitor – the Lord Bishop of Ely – was dining with the College Council. Wasn't that witty?'

'Even so, I don't think we'll have him in our taxi. Being with the *Manchester Guardian* has made him so *teaching*. What a pity he couldn't have been a larky little undergrad forever. You too, darling. You're getting positively *stout* with all your food and drink. To say nothing of those slag-spots on your bottom.'

Right, you slut, thought I: watch out for my searing revenge.

Suki and Coral went to their room at nine o'clock. I followed half an hour later and in the pitch dark stuck my left foot in a chamber pot (while removing my knicks), which had been copiously used by both girls, the loo being about a furlong away over the oasis. Having got my foot out of the potty but dropped my knicks into it, I salvaged both as best I could and played eenie-meenie-minie-mo with the two beds, not deliberately getting into the wrong one, you understand, but leaving it to chance whether or not Suki should be disciplined for her ill-natured personal remarks of earlier that evening. By the time I got to the controversial passage about the nigger and his toe, I was so confused that I had forgotten who was in which bed anyway. At the end of the jingle I slithered into the bed that the gods had allotted me, uncertain of the outcome – except that whatever it was it immediately clamped a mouth like a rubber plug-sucker on to my own, and off we went.

There was a sharp snore from the other bed, the kind that wakes the snorer, as indeed it did now.

'What's all this huffing and puffing?' said Suki's voice crossly.

'YYYrrrryoowwwwhh,' said Coral, and flopped about like an expiring whale.

'I distinctly told you earlier on,' said Suki, 'that my bed was the furthest from the door.'

'Sorry love. I forgot. Anyhow, you should have kept awake for me. Lover's vigil before the tryst – all that kind of a thing. Christ. Double Christ. I think I'm coming.'

'NOT YET!' yelled Coral.

'But I thought you were. All this Egyptian PT. I mean Sudanese PT.'

'I go on like this for at least five minutes first.'

'Start doing the twenty-nine times table, darling,' said Suki. 'They say it helps you to hold back.'

'29, 58, — er — 87, 116. It's not much good, I'm afraid.'

'KEEP GOING!' howled Coral. 'Another three minutes should do the trick.'

'There you are, Simon,' Suki said: 'you've got to last another three minutes to oblige her ladyship. Let me see; how can we slow you up? I know: by telling you something to put you off. So think of Coral pissing on the potty.'

I came instantly.

'You CUNT,' commented Coral. 'You've spent.'

'Extraordinary old-fashioned word,' gloated Suki.

'Never mind, Coral. I'm putting my finger in. Or would you prefer two?'

'I've got some knitting needles in my case,' said Suki, 'if they'd be any help.'

'Not fingers,' burbled Coral; 'give me tongue.'

'Just you dare!' shouted Suki.

'For Christ's sake let her come in peace,' I said, 'now that she's started.'

'All right, but no tongue. So keep on talking so's I can be sure there isn't.'

'Tongue, tongue, tongue,' implored Coral, 'lovely wet, warm tongue.'

I had an inspiration.

'This is not my fault,' I said for Suki's benefit. 'You should have given me precise directions.'

'Warm and wet, warm and wet,' cooed grateful Coral, and juddered like a jet on take-off.

'What could be more precise than "the bed furthest from the door"?'

'One loses one's sense of direction in the dark.'

'And one's sense of loyalty, it seems.'

'Warm, wet; wet, warm,' cooed Coral, and farted like an elephant.

'*E finita la comedia*,' said Suki. 'She once told me: she always farts as she comes.'

'It's quite common, I believe, though I prefer ladies to laugh, like you do.'

'It's too late to start sucking up now. But I might forgive you just a teeny bit if you'll tell me one thing. She was going right off the boil when you came too soon, so how did you manage it after all? All that warm and wet milarky?'

'Little Willie Wee-Wee,' I said.

When we left for Abu Simbel both the girls, sitting on either side of me in the back, were a bit sniffy, and Suki insisted on clutching my whatnot, presumably to make sure that Coral couldn't. For half an hour we bumped along a desert track, in an excruciating car driven by an excruciating Sudanese driver. When we reached the frontier post, Suki passed a wodge of Totopoly money to a fly-blown (even in the cool of the night) Egyptian, indicating the convoy of cars that carried the rest of the party in our wake; and on we went, with my whatnot now getting stiffer and stiffer, to a dawn crossing of the waters almost into the mouth of the temple, which the rising sun from behind us reddened to a shade of Westminster pink.

The temple whistled with the sudden warmth. My whatnot shrank. My bowels bubbled. Last night's dinner at Wigi Zigi was doing its work.

'God is punishing you for frotting about with Coral,' said Suki when I told her. 'No. There is no loo here. You will just have to go behind the temple.'

In practice, this meant climbing a sand mountain to the left of the temple and descending its reverse slope. When I got back to our party, my stomach churned maliciously and I had to make the same excursion all over again. Nevertheless, I got in on the end of a lecture which was delivered by a Scottish archaeologist in the grateful gloom of the temple and in which he explained how they were scheming to shift the building, piecemeal, to a new location, in order to save it from being drowned by the floods that would follow the opening of the new dam.

The United States, he explained, and several countries in Europe were putting up the billions needed in money; the removal would be planned by scholars, antiquarians, and engineers from Germany, Italy, England and America, and the actual rebuilding on the new site would be supervised by an international team of expert field archaeologists. The fetching, carrying, hewing, drawing, sweeping, watering, washing-up, but *not* the cooking, would be done by the usual squads of natives, on the strength of which the Egyptian Government was demanding parity of esteem in the operation. The organisers had also been warned by Cairo that no effort was to be made to inhibit the menials from claiming their 'just perquisites' – i.e. that there must be no precautions or sanctions applied against thieving, no matter how prevalent.

'What one endures from these people in the interests of art and preservation,' sighed the lecturer. 'However, since the Egyptians hope to gross trillions from tourism as a result of our efforts, they will take care not to make our task totally intolerable – though they will prove adept in effecting the periodic humiliation of some of our number by charges, not necessarily false, of pederasty and "social exploitation" . . .'

ii) And Adders

'. . . Numerous instances of pederasty and social exploitation,' said a blackamoor (Nubian? Numidian?) nearly twenty years later in 1980, 'made it necessary to require the international team to leave Egyptian territory, where in any case they had achieved next to nothing.* Only some small fraction of the funding of this magnificent operation was provided by the West: all else was the work of Libyans, Tunisians, Egyptians and other North Africans.'

'Bravo,' said the leader of the tour; 'and perhaps we could now go into the temple itself? The ladies and gentlemen have been standing in the hot sun for a very long time.'

'And there they will continue to stand,' said the blackamoor, 'until I have finished what I have to say.'

This took another twenty minutes, and was a farrago of how the Libyans (etc. etc.) had dismissed as futile the Westerners' 'decadent and misconceived' proposals on how to shift the temple from its old site, where I had been with Suki and Coral, to the new site, where I now was with Hamish – who had left Hamilton three years previously – and his friends Michael and Isabel Briggs. The Pan-North-African consortium, it appeared, had 'gone back to the drawing board' and, inspired 'by the Islamic faith and depending wholly on Marxist-Leninist methodology, had created the brilliant new principles whereby . . .' etc. etc. etc. Only when this obligatory puffing and

* The lies and 'disinformation' which this black gentleman was propounding for us were of such enormity that even he, clearly a man of intelligence and humour though also of boundless conceit, did not appear to be taking them very seriously.

posturing had been got through were the barricades unlocked and the high-paying tourists admitted the temple, from which they were immediately ordered out as the pilot of the aeroplane wished to be home early to attend a wedding feast. 'All must give way to observances of the True Religion,' mouthed the official mountebank – with, to be fair, a faint twinkle of irony – as he pointed to the vehicle that would carry us to our aircraft.

'Call back yesterday,' I sighed.

'Bring back Farouk?' suggested Isabel, who was called Colegate as well as Briggs.

'Yes. Heavenly colonisation. Delicious fascism. Above all, blissful racialism.'

'It's called "racism" these days,' Michael said.

' "Racialism" is too long a word for pupils at comprehensive schools to learn,' said Hamish.

'I know a girl called Jane,' I said, 'who had pneumatic thighs, that one wanted to *gnaw*, showing over the top of her stockings – for as long as that delightful fashion lasted. Since she loved her husband, who was called "Karl", she would not allow any gnawing of her luscious hams but, being an expert cook, she provided other fare to distract her many friends and admirers. The only trouble with Jane was that she was a fully paid-up socialist and one day, when her own children were nearly grown up, she went to teach in a comprehensive school, the first of its kind, I believe – the one in Ladbroke Grove. Now, Jane always said that the pupils there were really quite keen to learn; the fault lay with the teachers – that is what masters and mistresses are called in such schools, it seems – who could not, or would not, teach them. They – the teachers – used to hold union meetings almost every evening. Someone would get up and say, "Comrades, what action shall we take?" And Jane, who in those days preserved some idea of moderation, as well as being a sensible wife and mother, would get up and say: "Brothers and sisters, can we please be clear first of all, *why* and *whether* we need to take action?" This made her unpopular, and she was warned that if she went on like that, complaints would be laid against her and she would probably be sacked – because if the union took a pick at her the authorities would not dare keep her on.'

'So what happened then?' said Isabel, who liked this sort of story.

'Well, Jane was anxious to stay, as she'd made friends with many of her pupils and didn't want to let them down.'

We got out of the smelly Egyptian bus and into a smelly Egyptian aeroplane.

'So she psyched herself into thinking that the sin was hers and not the union's,' I went on, as we fought with rusty seat belts; 'she made herself believe that she was too obsessed with bourgeois logic and so on, and that if she only made herself even more socialist she'd be better able to cooperate at union meetings. Being a determined person, she forced herself further and further to the Left, until she became quite famous for her radical and inflammatory speeches and was asked to address meetings all over London, not just NUT meetings, but any gatherings of the disaffected, often way outside the lunatic margin. All this led to great sadness.'

The aeroplane shot forward, checked and shuddered several times, then flapped wildly into the air.

'She was arrested?' said Isabel, when she had recovered. 'Beaten up by the police? Or by the National Front?'

'No. Her cooking went downhill. In the old days, as I have indicated, she'd been a super cordon bleu chef. But she decided that cordon bleu cookery wasn't consistent with socialism, and in any case she was so busy going to more meetings and making up more speeches that she hadn't the time to cook, and even when she had her left-wing conscience would not allow her to produce any of the classical dishes: except *Cassoulet de Carcassone*, and at last she decided that even *that* was an insult to the working class. On the rare occasions when she did still cook, it was coarser and coarser peasant messes – until finally she went so downmarket that all she would serve was soul food. Very upsetting for poor Karl, and their greedy and discerning friends like me.'

'How did it end?' said Michael, who always hankered for conclusions.

'Karl went to a meeting of the PEN Club for the sake of the buffet, and met a writer of children's books who adored cooking and copulating afterwards. When Jane found out, she said she had been betrayed and wouldn't get out of bed for a week. No one took any notice and she was made to look very silly indeed.'

'Food is a problem with all married couples,' said Hamish. 'One of the reasons I left Hamilton at last was not only because she got so pissed, but because she started saying that her Jewish heredity was calling to her and from now on she could only eat kosher food. She had an absurd snobbery, you see, about being a Sephardic yid instead of the other kind; and the rabbi of the smart Sephardic synagogue called Penis Marx, or something of the sort, wouldn't let her join unless she went more orthodox. So first she wouldn't eat pork or bacon, then she barred lobster and prawns. Then she said she'd invited the rabbi of Penis Whatever to come round to the house and do a ritual purification of the kitchen and all the dishes. At this point I cooked ham with a cream sauce for luncheon on the day the rabbi was coming, and walked out forever.'

By leaving Hamilton, Hamish became not only free but also poor. His availability and his penury had almost cured my infatuation for him. Almost, but not quite. For one thing, he very soon acquired ample provision again: for when the house on Corfu was sold, he received half the proceeds – having prudently registered himself with the Greek housing authority as half the owner – and yet as this was the only property he possessed, he was not subject, as was Hamilton, to capital gains tax. All this brought about a return of my affection if not my ardour, which had always been bootless in any case, with the result that although I did not move in with Hamish, which would have been unendurable for both of us, I did take a *pied-à-terre* in Hove where he now lived when not abroad, in order to dine with him nightly. I provided the wine and he provided and cooked the food, an arrangement which committed nobody to anything, beneficently limited the time we spent together, and for a long time worked very smoothly.

More of all this, if you can bear it, later. Meanwhile, here we both were in December, 1980, on a trip down the Nile with Michael and Isabel; sharing a cabin, not out of lust, but because of Hamish's Scottish propensity to save money even when he had plenty. His meanness (not to put too fine a point on it) was apparently potent enough to anaesthetise him against my habitual snoring and even my orientally scented defecations in the tiny loo we shared – but as to that, I thought, it was his own choice.

'What did you think of Abu Simbel,' he asked, as we undressed that evening for our separate beds.

'I thought that it had lost its point. When I went to the temple with Suki seventeen years ago, it was where it was meant to be. When they moved it they left its Lares, its Genius, its ghosts and divinities behind. Those refused to go too, you see.'

'Everyone seems agreed that it's a remarkable reconstruction. Never mind that uppity sambo and his lies about all the work being done by Africans. Whoever did do the piecing together was, according to the experts, entirely accurate.'

'Granted,' I said. 'It is still a fine sight. So would the Parthenon be a fine sight if they took it to pieces and put it together again in the middle of Constitution Square. A fine sight – but dead.'

'Perhaps,' said Hamish, 'the temple of Abu Simbel is preferable without its gods and its ghosts. Whereas Greek gods are warm and human, even if vengeful and sadistic, Egyptian gods I find totally alien – saurian, crocodilian. Again, while Greek ghosts are recognisably the ghosts of men, Egyptian ghosts are inert, silent, sightless, deaf – wound and muffled in cerements like their mummies.'

'I don't quite know about that. You remember that double palace we saw: one for the vizier while he lived; the second, adjacent and almost identical, for him to move into when dead. That indicates a fairly lively conception.'

'No,' said Hamish. 'They were only going to move the corpse in. A corpse that wouldn't even twitter and flit about as the Greek ghosts did, but would just lie there the titular monarch of all it did *not* survey . . . like King Log in the fable. No, Simon: no Egyptian gods and no Egyptian ghosts for me. Every building along this river presents a blank face of death. In Ancient Greece even the graves are brushed by joy, telling us that life was sometimes sweet for the incumbent.'

Well, I thought as I lay in the dark, this is not the view of the Ancient Greeks which you were putting across in Olympia ten years ago. Perhaps your insights have improved in the last decade, or perhaps you really have no opinions at all save those that you improvise to support you in an enjoyable rôle on the given occasion.

PART FIVE

Among The Barbarians

i) The Army of Occupation

'We could perfectly well go skiing,' said O.

'We could. But the rest of us can't ski.'

'You could learn.'

'Too late,' I said. 'You have to start when you are two . . . if you want to do the thing properly.'

'I started just a few weeks ago. I'm not doing too badly.'

'You ski like your own maiden aunt in heat,' I said. 'Anyway, Flinny, Ralph and myself do not want to go skiing. We want to go to Baden-Baden.'

'And fug about in the casino all day. Skiing in the Harz Mountains would make you all far fitter.'

'We don't want to be fitter. Let me remind you, O, that Ralph and Flinny and I thought up this holiday. Nobody invited you. You have invited yourself. Johnny-come-lately.'

'Have you thought about the money?'

'Incessantly.'

'Baden-Baden is a famous spa town. It is *very* expensive.'

'The rate of exchange is in our favour. We get twelve and a half West German marks to the pound.'

This was the November of 1953. O and I were stationed with the First Battalion of our Regiment in Goettingen, almost on the border between East and West Germany. Goettingen, which was famous for its university and its appeal to syphilitic poets, particularly English ones, was a pleasant enough town . . . then. Our barracks, once a showpiece Wehrmacht *Casernen*, stood on a coniferous slope overlooking the town and were divided into three terraces. O and I were presently in one of the buildings on the bottom terrace, practising in an indoor range with a fierce and beautiful German pistol which O had purchased on the black market with a medium-sized tin of Army Issue cocoa and four dozen rolls of lavatory paper, officers for the use of. It was, you perceive, a good time to be in Germany.

'The field cashier,' said O, 'is instructed strictly to limit the number of marks which he gives in exchange.'

'The field cashier,' said I, 'is not the only source of German currency. The German waiters in the mess will give us twenty marks to the pound.'

'We could be court-martialled for dealing with them.'

'We could be court-martialled for possessing this unregistered pistol. We could be court-martialled for just about everything we've done since getting out of bed this morning.'

'Like what?' said O.

'Like tricking the Arms-Kote orderly into issuing ammunition which we thought might fit this automatic.'

'It fits it admirably.'

'That is not the point. We could have been court-martialled for syphoning petrol out of the company commander's Land Rover and into your car. And for dating up that little German number employed by the NAAFI.'

'No, we couldn't,' said O. 'We are now allowed to fraternise with the Krauts. It's not like 1946.'

'We are allowed – even encouraged – to be friendly with the Germans. With German adults, that is. We are not allowed to plan the seduction of fourteen-year-old Frauleins.'

'She didn't look that young. She had tits like the Venus of Milo.'

'Lots of fourteen-year-olds do. It is important to discriminate. Ignorance, in this matter, is no defence – or not for a man of your experience.'

O fired five rounds.

'A bull and four inners,' he said, having pulled the target in for inspection. 'Not bad.'

'Rather than have you interfere with fourteen-year-old NAAFI girls,' I said, 'we shall certainly allow you to gate-crash our holiday.

But you must make up your mind to put your hand in your pocket and pay for your own single room at the Brenner's Park Hotel in Baden-Baden.'

'All right. If you'll pay me the seventy-five pounds you owe me for Chemmy. I've had the IOU for two months.'

'Ralph is also coming on me to redeem an IOU – the one I gave him after that game of Vingt-et-un in which he cheated.'

'I remember. He kept back some low cards to fake a "five-and-under". Can't we lose Ralph?' O said.

'No. He is driving us there in his car.'

'What about Flinny? Has anyone got any of *his* IOUs?'

'I have four. I can't press him for money,' I said, 'because it would be like whipping a spaniel. Ralph, needless to say, will not accept them in exchange for mine.'

'Nor will I,' O said. 'How are you planning to pay for this trip?'

'I have borrowed money from RQMS Lazarus Risen Plumb. He is very kind to young officers in need. But I have not got enough to redeem any IOUs.'

'Why is he called "Lazarus Risen"?'

'His parents belonged to a peculiar sect in Ledbury. It's like being called "Fear of the Lord" or "Word of the Saviour", only in Plumb's case a rather more baroque imagination was applied.'

'Well,' said O, 'you might share with a chap.'

'You can perfectly well go the RQMS yourself.'

'How much do you think he's good for?'

'Fifty quid.'

'Would he be interested in this automatic?'

'No. He is a man of peace.'

'Whisky? Cocoa? Soap? Loo paper?'

'He has plenty of the first in the sergeants' mess, and plenty of the rest in his own stores.'

'I know,' said O. 'That's where I got all my stuff from, to barter for this pistol. I pretended to be selecting a bedding roll for Exercise Black Bull, and I filled it up with a lot of other goodies and smuggled them out.'

There was a fiendish glint of cunning from behind O's spectacles.

'He knows all about that,' I said. 'He told me.'

'Oh. Doesn't he mind?'

'He is simply amused that anyone could be so petty. He would have given you that cocoa and the rest, if you'd only asked him. As it is . . . well, he is a man of Christian forbearance.'

'Then would he be impressed if I offered him some of it back? If I said I was repenting?'

'He dislikes hypocrites. He adores officers – even shady ones like you. Just ask to borrow fifty pounds and give him a postdated cheque as security. He may be able to give it to you in marks – at a beneficial rate – straight out.'

'If we went skiing — '

'We are going to Baden-Baden.'

'How are you going to get out of honouring that IOU of yours which Ralph's got? He's not so softhearted as I am.'

'No. He is a vulture and you are only a crocodile. I'm going to offer to introduce him to that fourteen-year-old NAAFI girl.'

'You . . . you *swine!*' said O.

'She's been had by half the battalion, so Lance-Corporal Pauly told me when we were having a little feel together. One more – an officer at that – won't hurt her.'

'Suppose she's got VD? And gives it to Ralphy boy? Serve the brute right.'

'The possibility of clap – or worse – is one of the reasons why I'm trying to discourage you. As for Ralph, he is far too canny ever to catch anything. He always wears a French letter for a start.'

'How do you know?'

'Flinny told me. Flinny once settled a debt of ten pounds which he owed Ralph by supplying Ralph with two hundred French letters from the Medical Centre. Ralph told Flinny he always used them, even with that stuck-up girlfriend of his in London. You know, Lady Exmoor's secretary. She's quite safe, Ralph said, but he doesn't want her to get preggers and in any case she has a very sexy way of putting them on to him. Ralph says that's really the best bit. He usually comes there and then.'

'That can't please her.'

'On the contrary. She doesn't really care, it seems, for fornication as such. Putting the john on Ralph's erection is her best thing too.'

'Some people,' said O, 'are just filthy perverts. What you all need is a good, cheap, healthy holiday with lots of exercise and fresh air.'

'There are lovely walks in the Kur Garten at Baden. All marked out and graded. Half a mile on the flat for severe conditions of the heart; a mile on a slight slope if you're recovering. A mile and a half to cure constipa — '

' — You call that exercise?'

'One doesn't need that much. Not even to give one an appetite. The food which Herr Brenner serves is so delicious it just melts in the mouth.'

The Brenner's Park Hotel is one of the most luxurious in Europe, and was so even in 1953. Only the artificial rate of exchange available to Army personnel made it a feasible hostelry for subalterns. Herr Brenner, a motherly old thing, did not resent this, but enjoyed advising us – of the difference, for example, between caviar and *fresh* caviar (the latter imported during the previous three days) and of the correct wine (sweet) to drink with foie gras. He liked indulging us, and we liked being indulged – though Flinny O'Flanagan, a resolute Roman Catholic but in other respects a worldly and urbane man, had a theory that this was his way of getting his revenge on the British for winning the war. He planned to ruin our generation of young officers, Flinny said, by turning us into monsters of obesity with livers as swollen as the Strasbourg geese he got his foie gras from.

'Caviar, at least, does no harm,' said Ralph, tucking in.

'All that oil,' said O, 'hardens the arteries.'

Flinny the physician nodded reluctant agreement.

'Herr Brenner will bring about the doom of us all,' he pronounced, hammering his thesis home.

'The thing about spa towns,' I said, 'is that they cure you, then tempt you, then keep you for a further cure. And so on forever, if they had their way.'

'Before going to the gaming rooms in the Spiel Bank this afternoon,' O said, 'we must all go for a walk. Not one of the sedate perambulations marked out in the Kur Park for nonagenarians, but a proper, Light Infantry-pace training march.'

'Not a bad idea,' said Ralph. And even I agreed with him; for although Herr Brenner's food did indeed melt in the mouth, lack of exercise was making problems with my digestion.

'I'm glad you both assent,' said O. 'Ralph, if you will be so good as to drive us a little way into the Black Forest, we can make a convenient circuit with plenty of fit-making gradients. I have a map to make sure we don't get lost.'

'I think,' said Flinny O'Flanagan, 'that I shall take a nap instead. This is, after all, a holiday, and I have been much overworked at Goettingen this last month.'

' "Medical officer's rounds",' sneered Ralph: 'shagging all the wives in married quarters.'

'They need a little reassurance from time to time,' said Flinny, 'like anybody else.'

'Of course,' said O, winking at me (why?), 'we can dispense with the MO on this little training scheme. After all, he doesn't need to be fit: he spends his whole time on manoeuvres lying on his bunk in the ambulance and having fantasies about succubi.'

'Sure, 'tis a mortal sin to harbour the devil's creeturs,' burred Flinny, in the brogue he only affected when the supernatural was under discussion. 'The penance for spilling the seed in lustful reverie is greater than that for carnal knowledge of a damsel.'

'In any case at all,' said O, '*you* do not need a ten-mile training march.'

'Ten miles?' I cried. 'Let's not get too intense about this. I agreed with you that it would be nice to get out of overheated German buildings and unclog our viscera. But ten miles — '

' — Do not worry,' said O, winking at me again with his closed eye, hidden from Ralph by his own gargantuan proboscis. 'I shall devise a course well within everyone's capacity.' And to Flinny, 'You must promise not to go to the gaming rooms till we get back. I fear you are becoming addicted.'

'I'll stay fast in my bedroom, on the honour of an Irish gentleman.'

'From Liverpool,' sneered Ralph.

'Then,' said O to Ralph and me, before Flinny could take offence, 'I shall expect the pair of you to be ready in Ralph's car outside the main entrance to the hotel in seven minutes flat, and dressed in suitable forest-walking gear.'

As I came through the foyer five minutes later in my suitable forest-walking gear of knicker-bockers and a silly Hun hat with a boar's bristle, the head porter beckoned to me and gave me a note.

'Condign punishment of the odious and avaricious cheat, Ralph Marlingham,' said the note, 'is about to commence. Do exactly what I tell you during the walk in the Black Forest. O.'

Ralph's car was already outside (like O, he was a very punctual soldier), with Ralph in the driving seat and O beside him.

'Twenty seconds late, old bean,' said O as I approached: 'slut.'

We drove out of Baden-Baden, up the Oos, a tributary of the Murg which is itself a tributary of the Rhine, steadily mounting. The Forest, not yet rotten with industrial discharge, began to close in on the road. After about five miles of motoring uphill, O said to Ralph:

'Next suitable place for parking.'

A furlong further on Ralph turned right down a track and then right again into a small clearing. It was now three-thirty; dusk was falling. Pleased, even excited, by the prospect of air and space after three days of hotel rooms and roulette tables, I had forgotten how early the night came over Germany during the winter.

'This is just silly,' I said. 'We haven't been thinking straight. Let's go back to Baden-Baden.'

'I have not only a map but a compass,' said O. 'We shall do splendidly.'

'Indeed we shall,' said Ralph, eager to toady to O (the senior man) and to gain face over me.

'A quick drink first,' said O, passing a flask to Ralph. 'Cherry Brandy.'

Ralph drank.

'You two get out,' Ralph said; 'I'll just lock up.'

O and I stood looking at a huge, red, science-fiction sun as it sank towards the Rhine beneath us.

'My turn with that flask,' I said.

'No, dear. No Cherry Herring for you.'

'Why not?'

'Nanny says it's bad for you. Just do as Nanny tells you.'

Ralph joined us.

'I feel a bit queasy,' he said.

'All that lunch,' said O. 'A little healthy exercise will soon set you right.'

After we had followed a path, under O's direction, about fifty yards into the Forest, Ralph sat down on a tree trunk and put his head in his hands. Almost immediately he fell asleep in the same position.

'Flinny gave me a powder,' said O, 'which I persuaded him to bring all the way from Goettingen, to put in the Cherry Herring. Loathsome, sickly stuff, Cherry Herring, but we needed something to disguise the bitterness of that powder.'

'*We* needed?' I said. '*You* did. What on earth do you think you're doing, slipping Ralph a Mickey Finn — '

' — Mickey Flinn, ha ha . . .'

' — Ralph may not be the straightest chap on earth, but he's of our party (to which you belong only on sufferance) and he's driven us, quite comfortably and competently, the whole way from Goettingen to Baden-Baden. And,' I added, 'he's got to drive us back. So if you have permanently deprived him of his wits with that stuff of Flinny's — '

' — Peace, old bean. No harm will come to him. Just help me carry him back to his car and put him in the back. Then I shall drive us away before the vampires begin to prowl.'

'I do not understand why we have come all the way up here just to administer dope to Ralph.'

'Help me carry him to his car, and it will all be made very plain to you . . . Where does he keep the key?' said O, as we laid Ralph on the ground by the rear off-side wheel.

'How should I know?'

O began to go through Ralph's pockets, first through those of the camouflage combat jacket (in very new and short supply in those days) which Ralph was wearing over his sports jacket and corduroys, then through all the pockets of both jackets, including the inner ones. 'He won't feel a thing after swallowing this magic mixture of Flinny's.' Then in the trouser pockets.

'Funny,' said O. 'He must have dropped them somewhere.'

We walked back to the tree trunk on which Ralph had fallen asleep, then returned once more to the car, eyes-down looking all the way. The sun sank; the Rhine, and all the streams and ways in the Plain of Strasbourg, grew dark. O looked under the car.

'Have you got a torch?' he said.

'Of course not. You're the boy scout on this trip.'

'Matches? You smoke.'

'Here you are. Mind the petrol tank.'

'Not a sign. They *must* be in one of his pockets.'

O went through these again.

'It's getting very cold. We'd better wake him up,' I said, 'and ask him where they are.'

'We can't wake him up. The stuff in the Cherry B will put him right out for six hours. Flinny guaranteed it.'

'You're one cunt and Flinny's another.'

'Temper, temper . . . The first moment things go a little wrong . . .'

'What was the big idea, anyway?'

'To deliver him back to the hotel; put him in bed; then, when he came to, tell him that he'd passed out on the march and that while we were getting him out of the Forest some one had come along and drained the petrol tank and pinched the wheels – whereas really we would have sold the petrol and the wheels on the black market and made a packet in cash.'

'I see. So Ralph fainted a short way along that path, we tell him, with all of us still in full sight of his car, and somebody came along and emptied the tank and cranked off the wheels without you and me knowing, while we carried Ralph towards it.'

'He was meant to get a little further before he passed out.'

'Brilliant. It nearly killed me carrying him back just now, but *you* had intended me to carry him ten times the distance.'

'You hardly helped at all, you're such a floppy weed.'

'Such a floppy weed I was *meant* to be going to help you carry him a league or two.'

'Don't be so silly. Not nearly so f — '

' — AND, I suppose we were going to tell him we drove him back to Baden-Baden in a car that had no wheels and no petrol.'

'For Christ's sake. We were going to tell him we'd stopped a passing car and brought him back in that, leaving *his* car up here for the polizei to bring in.'

'So that's what we were going to tell him, was it? And what would we really have done?'

'Driven to a black-market garage. Sold the wheels and the petrol and anything else they wanted. Rung up a taxi and gone back to the hotel in that. And then told Ralph, when he woke up, that his car had already been picked up in the Forest and was in the garage, *where it in fact was*, while the garage people waited for his orders. Very neat, you see.'

'Yes,' said Ralph, 'I do see.' He got to his feet. 'What a lucky thing I keep the key in the money pocket of my jacket, just inside the sleeve. It's the new thing, Gieves told me, specially made to protect one against thieves and pickpockets in the dishonest age ushered in by egalitarian indulgence. It appears to work. Gieves will be delighted when I tell them.'

By this time Ralph had unlocked the car and got in. He now slammed the door and drove off.

'You're pathetic,' said O. 'Why didn't you stop him?'

'Why didn't you?'

'I was having cramp after crawling under the car.'

'And I was feeling sick after carrying Ralph. You *would* make me the one to walk backwards.'

When O and I reached the hotel around midnight – no passing car having stopped for us – we were, of course, far too late for dinner but not too late to find Flinny in the bar.

'When you didn't show up,' he said, 'I thought you wouldn't mind me going to the casino without you. Then I lost all my money and so I came back.'

'Why didn't you give me a proper draught,' said O, 'to put in the Cherry Herring? It only knocked him out for a few minutes.'

'My professional conscience would not allow me to be a party to such goings on. To say nothing of my religion.'

'Both your professional conscience and your religion apparently allow you to screw every wife in married quarters on your afternoon rounds.'

'I get carried away by compassion for the poor sex-starved creatures. Their husbands are all so full of beer, do you see, that their parts are a-dangle with brewer's droop.'

'I see. Lust has nothing to do with it?'

'Oh, no. Jesus, Joseph and the Holy Virgin be my witness. I am driven by pure pity and Christian love.'

'But not love of truth. Why did you *say* you had given me a good powerful draught when you knew you hadn't?'

'Because you are so horrible to a poor fellow when you are not having your way.'

'Well,' said O, 'now you've been punished for your lies and lechery. You've lost all your money. *I* haven't any to spare for you. Perhaps Simon has? – I *don't* think.'

'Just enough to pay his hotel bill when we leave,' I said, by now hating O so much for the loss of my dinner that I was anxious, even if it cost me good money, to disoblige him by succouring Flinny. 'I had that lucky win last night, when fourteen came up three times running.'

Flinny sank down on to his knees in front of me.

'*Mea culpa*,' he howled; '*mea maxima culpa*.'

'Don't be so absurd,' said O. 'Get up at once.'

'I lost all my money *twice*,' sobbed Flinny, 'the first time quite early in the evening. So I came back here and they let me have your keys, yours and O's, because I invented some blarneyfying tale and the Germans have such respect for doctors – which they knew me to be because of my passport which they demanded on my arrival, me having left my identity card in the bed of Mrs Colour Sergeant Podge.'

'What were you doing with your *identity card* in that ghastly woman's bed?'

'She likes the feel of the celluloid cover up her — '

'For God's sake let him get on,' said O. 'All this silly chat about I/D cards and passports and Colour Sergeant Podge's beastly woman's c — '

' — Never say that wicked woorrrd and shaaame God's Moither,' moaned Flinny; 'besides, 'twas not therrrre Dame Podge wished the celluloid, 'twas up her rect — '

' — FLINNY,' I said. 'WHAT DID YOU DO WITH OUR KEYS WHEN YOU HAD THEM?'

'I went to your rooms, so I did, and borrowed all your money, all of it, and then I went back to the beautiful gaming rooms, beautiful as Heaven itself, with God and all His Sai — '

'FLINNY!'

' — And got a message from St Patrick's own self, saying "Flinny, my son, go banco against the Chemmy banker", which I did with all the money, for 'twas the Saint's own command which he laid upon me to mortify me for my most grievous sins – when the vile Teuton that was banker turned up a nine to my nought, and the devil's factor lifted my pretty counters, worth a thousand Deutschmarks, from the green baize that was like the pastures of Paradise — '

' — You were so greedy,' I said, 'that you pinched *all* our money?'

'And so crazed,' said O, 'that you risked the whole lot in a single coup?'

'In one word,' said Flinny. 'Yes.'

'I'm beginning to think,' said O, 'that all those stories – about how people's brains turn to water if they do it too much – are true.'

'You can't talk,' I said, 'after that ludicrous scheme of yours for swindling Ralph.'

'It would have worked perfectly well if this fornicating turd of a snivelling papist punter had given me the proper dope for Ralph.'

'Where is Ralph?' I said.

'Paid up and gone,' said Flinny. 'Or so they said at the bureau. I asked for his room keys too, do you see.'

'No transport and no money,' said O, suddenly beaming (he always liked being in a jam). 'But I've got the perfect plan. It will depend,' he said to Flinny, 'on your ditching both your professional conscience and your religion . . . which in all the circumstances is the very least you can do for us.'

'What can you mean?' said Flinny.

'Tomorrow morning,' said O, 'you will go into Baden-Baden to the knitting-needle shop. Meanwhile, I'll have a quiet word with the concierge about contacts . . . contacts with ladies who have been deceived and deserted and left with unwanted pledges of temporary affection by local French poilus – this being, as even you will know, the French Zone of Occupied Germany. Are you beginning to get the message, Flinny? The concierge may demand quite a large cut of the profit of this operation – the *mot juste*, I think – but I dare say I can hold him down to, say, forty per cent. After all, despite all the sanctimonious talk of an alliance with a re-arisen and emergent Germany, this *is* still a defeated enemy country (one of the nastiest in history), and we need not take any lip from a mere concierge.'

ii) The Ambassadors of England

What have I done for you,
England, my England?
What is there I would not do,
England, my own?

W.E. Henley; For England's Sake (1900);
        iii Pro Rege Nostro

A little under fifteen years after the excursion upon which I have just been dilating, I arrived at the Brenner's Park Hotel one winter's evening with Hamilton Glott.

Although Herr Brenner was long dead, the food was as good as ever. Unfortunately, the rate of exchange was not. Hamilton, showing off in front of his travel agent, had asked him to book a single bedroom for me and a suite for himself. Now that he was in it, he got cold feet.

'We must find out what it's going to cost me,' he said after a delicious dinner, as he surveyed his two bedrooms, his drawing-room, his dining-room and what looked like his ballroom.

'Ask at the desk.'

'That would be to lose face,' Hamilton said. 'I must appear not to care about the price.'

'Then you can ask them if they'll take a cheque drawn on your English bank.' Although this was still technically illegal in 1967, it was often quietly arranged between well-shod Englishmen and obliging foreigners who ran places like Brenner's. 'If they will,' I said, 'you won't need to know what the bill will be.'

'But then I'd be committed. If they agree to take a cheque, I can't back out.'

'If they agree to take a cheque you won't need to back out, because then there'll be no worry about currency.'

Hamilton's mouth twitched like a parsimonious weasel's.

'There'd still be worry about money,' he said.

'Look,' I said. 'On the day after tomorrow, Christmas Eve, Hamish is joining us here with the Vicar. Hamish has been told that he is to share a suite with you. He will have something unkind to say if you have moved out of it. The Vicar has been told (many times) that Hamish is to share a suite with you. He too will have something unkind to say, to your dear friends all over London: Hamilton, the Vicar will say, was too mean to keep the suite which he had booked in the Brenner's Park Hotel. As for Hamish, he will probably knock you senseless – before retiring to lock himself, for the whole of Christmas, into the mingy single room you will presumably arrange for him instead.'

'At least,' said Hamilton, wobbling all over, 'let us find out how much this costs. There should be a notice up somewhere. The law stipulates.'

'The German law does indeed stipulate that the price of all accommodation should be posted prominently inside that accommodation; usually,' I said, 'on the back of the door. There is an exception, however, in the case of luxury accommodation; the idea being that princes or noblemen might be offended if the price of their lodging was pushed into their faces.'

'Who said anything about princes or noblemen?'

'Surely you noticed? Outside your front door it says "Margrave's Suite". The eldest son of the Grand Duke of Baden, you see, is called "The Margrave of Baden-Baden".'

'I *did* notice; but I thought that was just a gimmick to attract American Jews.'

'The cost will be the same for English Jews.'

'If only we could find it . . . After all, if they're not really expecting noblemen but only Jews, they might put up a tariff after all.'

So we looked behind the doors and into all the cupboards and wardrobes, and chests of drawers and silver canteens, and the desks in both bedrooms, the drawing-room, the ballroom, the dining-room and a small study which I discovered. No price list.

'What about the bathroom?'

'Why should they put it in there?'

'Why not?'

And in the bathroom indeed it was, stuck up at the back of the medicine chest and stating that the daily charge for the Margraval Suite was thirty-five pounds (all currencies were quoted) *per diem*, for single or double occupancy, including taxes but excluding refreshments of any kind. Now, in these days one would be very happy to get a broom-cupboard at the Brenner's Park Hotel for thirty-five pounds a day – in fact one couldn't. But in 1967, thirty-five pounds was worth at least four hundred in to-day's debauched money and so was rather a lot.

'We're going to be here ten days, so that's only three hundred and fifty pounds exclusive of refreshments,' I said.

'Hamish will expect French champagne, midnight snacks of smoked salmon and lobster; he'll probably set up a bar in here and invite anyone he happens to fancy, quite apart from hogs like you and the Vicar — '

'But if they'll take an English cheque, Hamilton, what can it matter? Think what the Vicar will say if you move into an ordinary room.'

The Vicar was an anglicised American friend of Hamish and Hamilton's who had wasted his substance and was only given a second lot of substance by his family on the strict condition that he found and pursued a career. Somehow or other he had found the Church of England. This calling had diminished neither his snobbery, his lechery, nor his malice.

'I'll sleep on it,' Hamilton said.

'Of course,' I said, 'even if you do decide to leave this suite that's no reason why we should leave this hotel?'

'Yes, it is. Loss of face. It would be intolerable staying on here.'

'I see. Just because *you* are too stingy to pay up, *I* have to be inconvenienced too. I sent off some laundry this evening. What shall I do if — '

' — You can ask for it back.'

'It won't be ready.'

'You can still have it back. Anyway, I haven't made up my mind yet.'

'Let alone what the Vicar will say,' I said, 'I should think Hamish will probably leave you if you give up this suite. I know I should. Imagine coming all the way from London, expecting to spend Christmas in a princely suite, and then finding that your lover has been too – too – too JEWY to keep his promise.'

'Stop being anti-Semitic.'

'*You* were anti-Semitic just now.'

'I'm allowed to be. I'm a Jew.'

'And don't I know it. The sort of Jew that made the Germans start Belsen.'

'Get out of my Margraval Suite.'

'Don't think I'm jealous.'

'Oh yes, you are. You want Hamish.'

In 1967 this wasn't true.

'I have just been trying,' I said, 'to ensure that you do not displease Hamish. I want him to stay with you. And even if I did fancy Hamish, I should still want him to stay with you, so that you had to keep him and pay for his treats and his suites.'

'We are going round in silly circles,' said Hamilton, not without dignity. 'As I say, I shall sleep on this matter and tell you my mind in the morning.'

In the morning there was a telegram to say that Hamish, who had been making a pre-Christmas Christmas visit to his mother, had now developed virulent influenza and could not join us. Later we had a second telegram, this from the Vicar, to say that he himself was still coming and had invited Mrs Viva King to take up Hamish's railway ticket and accommodation.

'What does he mean, "take up Hamish's accommodation"?' said Hamilton. 'That old bag cannot share my suite.'

'Why not? There are two separate bedrooms. But I surmise that the Vicar intends to share the suite with you and dump Viva in his own single. The Vicar has always rather fancied you: he once told me that since he was Jewish, too, you made him feel cosily incestuous. So he'll come prowling out of the Margravine's bedroom and into the Margrave's – or will it be the other way round? – and — '

'For Christ's sake shut up,' said Hamilton. 'For a start, Viva King cannot afford to stay in any part, no matter how exiguous, of this hotel. And since Hamish is not coming to join me in my suite, we can now move out, you and I, and tell everyone that we did so in order to alleviate any resentment that Hamish might have felt at thinking of me luxuriating in the Margraval Suite without him.'

'The vicar will still say it's sheer meanness – and so it will be.'

But in my heart of hearts I was not sorry when we left Brenner's later that morning – Hamilton having organised the retrieval of my laundry, in his facile German, as a gesture of good will – and moved into the *Forellen Hopf*, a suburban tavern on the Black Forest bank of the Oos. I was glad to save money, for a start; and was already beginning to be oppressed by the ghosts that loitered in Brenner's – the ghosts of Flinny, Ralph and O, three gamy young men (at their worst) who had now turned into sour middle-aged capons (at their best) . . . to say nothing of the mocking attentions paid to me by the shade of my own gaudy prime.

The next evening we met the Vicar and Viva at the station. Viva was a tedious and conceited old woman who had once been a pushy and pretentious young one and thought of herself, on the strength of her experience between the two, as a woman of the world. As the Vicar had once explained to me, she was frigid about men and prudish about women, but adored anyone of either sex who had had an operation to change it.

'She likes people who have been neutered, you see,' the Vicar used to say; 'it makes her feel safe, because she knows that they won't violate her own neutrality.'

The first few days we passed in eating carp, venison and boar in tourist restaurants staffed by hunking Teutons, and in listening to the Vicar's elegant malignities which were interrupted, all too often, by Viva's self-centred and mendacious histories of her life in various watering places, Baden-Baden not least, before the war. The only bits of these I enjoyed were her intermittent chorus lines about how Hamilton and the Vicar would not have been allowed near the place. 'Even titled Hebrews were warned off,' Viva said. 'I remember how offended the Rothschilds were. They thought that once you had been ennobled it purged any Jewish blood.'

Then we came to my birthday, the 28th of December. I had said nothing of its advent, but Hamilton already knew the date. I deprecated fuss or even mention, but by that time we were all so bored with each other that any diversion was to be prized. There were presents: cheap German cigars from the Vicar; a miniature chalet for keeping paper spills, which came out of its chimney, from Viva; and a manicure set from Hamilton, who always chose gifts with generosity and care,

152

comprising superb steel scissors, files, assorted instruments, and a black leather case with my name in gold. I still have this; if Hamilton is good at giving presents, I am good at guarding them. It was also decreed that there should be a Birthday Treat: dinner, paid for by the others' subscription (Viva's being theoretical), and the casino, which we had not yet visited.

Viva, though she had not been to the casino since the Thirties, of course had to know more about it than anybody else. 'One does not need passports or Identity Cards,' she announced, 'and even if one did, I should not, as they will remember me and have my name on record.' Diffidently, I pointed out that in 1953 the officials of the Spiel bank in the Kur Haus at Baden-Baden had been more bureaucratic and bloody-minded about identification than those in any other casino which I had ever visited before or since. 'That was in 1953,' snapped Viva; 'anyway, as I have told you already, they will certainly remember me.' Rather less diffidently, I remarked that memorable though she no doubt was, it was unlikely that even the most sharp-witted receptionist would have kept her image in mind for over a generation, and that, even were such a one still extant, he would probably have retired. Never mind, scoffed Viva, her name would be on the files. The records of visitors in the Thirties, I suggested, had perhaps been destroyed or lost by now as there had been, she might care to recall, some confusion in German affairs; and even if the file survived and her name were on it, she would still have to identify herself as the person named.

'I shall get in without my passport,' she said.

'Why not take it, Viva, just in case?' said the Vicar softly and sensibly.

'Because I know I shall not need it,' Viva said.

Hamilton, the kind of man who deliberately presents himself without a tie at smart restaurants in order to cause a row and draw attention to himself, supported Viva.

'Of course a person of Viva's seniority and distinction will be admitted without identification,' he said.

'Thank you, Hamilton dear,' said Viva.

'I will bet you one hundred pounds,' I said to Hamilton, 'that Viva will not be admitted into the gaming rooms without a passport or other means of identification which incorporates a photograph. I warn you before you take the bet,' I said, 'that I am quoting more or less verbatim from the notice displayed on the admissions counter.'

'Fifteen years ago,' said Hamilton.

'Will you take the bet?'

'Yes. Even if the regulation remains in force, they will make an exception of Viva.'

Viva simpered.

'Oh will they?' said the Vicar. 'Then I expect you'll be happy to bet another one hundred pounds with me?'

'Of course,' said Hamilton, with a flourish of hands and wrists.

'So,' I said. 'Hamilton bets the Vicar and myself one hundred pounds each that Viva will be admitted into the gaming rooms in Baden-Baden without identification; the Vicar and myself maintaining that she will be excluded from the gaming rooms until she produces identification. Correct?'

'Correct,' said the Vicar.

'Correct,' said Hamilton, raising one arm and allowing the hand to droop down on to his head.

'Right,' said the Vicar. 'Time to change. Germans are very keen on *tenue*. Luckily, I have brought my evening dress.'

By this I thought he meant a dinner jacket or even, being the eccentric he was, a tail coat. He appeared in clerical evening dress. 'With trousers as opposed to breeches and stockings,' he explained. The net result was a narrow and stylish, black frock coat, open at the front to show a black silk expanse, much decorated with bobbles and flounces, and topped by a clerical collar.

'This is the High Church version,' the Vicar said, 'with a few personal adjustments.' He indicated the bobbles and flounces. 'A mild concession to occasions of festivity,' he said, playing his fingers over them, 'but nevertheless' – his hand went to the collar – 'unmistakably the garb of a priest in orders.'

At dinner in a restaurant which specialised in unhung game birds (ah God, for lovely Herr Brenner!), the Vicar entertained us with some of the highlights of his career. He had been removed from a curacy in Soho when discovered showing an unusual film about boy scouts to the choir in the vestry. His plea that it was a training film – 'These boy scouts, my lord, exercised fully naked, like the Greeks' – was discounted by the bishop, who had low church leanings. However, with the help of an influential acquaintance, who belonged to the Vicar's sauna club, he had been transferred to a living in Chelsea. Here he had taken advantage of his second Sunday's coinciding with the first day of April, and had preached a controversial sermon on the subject of the trade unions, then much in the news; concluding with a spirited peroration in which he had urged that the whole TU Congress should be embarked on to hulks such as had been used for transportation, towed twenty leagues out to sea, and sunk. Many of his congregation had enjoyed this address but one of those who hadn't had reported him to the bishop – not the one that had handled the boy scout rumpus but a new incumbent still open-minded in regard to the Vicar. Seeking explanation, he was assured by the Vicar that this sermon had been preached on All Fools' Day and therefore under licence: in a word it was a joke or (in another) a jape.

'Was your sermon preached before noon?' enquired the courteous old gentleman.

'Yes, my lord. Matins began at ten-thirty; I preached at eleven ante meridiem, and was done in ten minutes.'

'Then the thing is quite clear. The licence of All Fools' Day (to be compared with that of the Roman Saturnalia) provides for all manner of liberty to be practised until noon . . . even within sacred precincts. Thus you will be familiar with the custom of electing a quirister to be boy bishop, and to preach or command, during the forenoon, in whatever fashion he pleases. *Quae cum ita sint*, dear boy; *nunc absolvimus te in nomine patris, et cetera, et cetera*, but in future please try to refrain from annoying your more humourless parishioners, as these are apt to pester me with their mean and trifling delations.'

When we reached the Kur Haus, we were all admitted by a cringing German doorman.

'There you are,' said Hamilton: 'no identification required. One hundred pounds, please, from both Simon and the Vicar.'

'The Kur Haus,' said the Vicar, 'like my Father's House, has many mansions, comprehending a ballroom, a concert room, a tap room (for drinking the disgusting waters), and a bath hall . . . as well as the Spiel casino, Spiel bank or gaming rooms, which we have yet to attain.

Please, Hamilton, do not carry greed to the point of fraudulent utterance, however easily susceptible of refutation.'

After walking about a mile we entered the foyer of the gaming rooms. Hamilton led Viva up to the most benign-looking of the three receptionists.

'This is the celebrated Mrs Viva King,' he promulgated, 'who frequented these rooms before – er – the catastrophe of 1939 to 1945. She is sure you will have no difficulty in finding her name on your files.'

'That is immaterial, *Mein Herr*. A new record of admission must be made (and paid) for any person who has not been here during the last administrative quinquennium.'

'Quinquennium?'

'Five years. *Mein Herr*.'

'But surely,' said honey-tongued Hamilton in his stylish Hannoverian German, 'in the case of a lady so venerable as Mrs Viva King. . . ?'

'That too is immaterial. I regret, *Mein Herr*. But no doubt gnädige Frau King has her passport with her, as any prudent person will always carry it – and is in any case required by law to do so – in a foreign country.'

But Mrs King, knowing she was right, had not bothered to bring it.

Meanwhile, the Vicar was having difficulties. The receptionist whom he had chosen was not sure that he could allow a clerical collar as the equivalent of the mandatory tie.

To cheer the Vicar up, I said, 'Hamilton has definitely lost his money. I can't imagine why he took the bet.'

'This man is an imbecile,' said the Vicar, indicating his receptionist, who was in deep confabulation with an inferior manager who now went off through an important-looking door. 'These Huns are the bally limit. None of them dares take responsibility for anything. We'd better watch Hamilton. He'll be looking for ways of greasing out.'

Hamilton came up to us. 'The man says,' he told us, 'that if you swear that Mrs King is now your wife but that there has not yet been time to transfer her on to your passport, he may be able to obtain permission to let her in on the strength of your identification . . . as Mrs Simon Raven.'

'What sort of fool am I going to look, saying I'm married to that old frump? It's not even as if she's got any money.'

'I only want you to be friendly and helpful,' said Hamilton, 'and save me the trouble of taking Viva back to the *Forellen Hopf* to fetch her passport. Besides, how does that receptionist know that Viva hasn't got any money?'

'How *could* I allow him to think that I married her – with money or without it? Whichever way you look at it, I should be an object of contempt.'

'Would you be prepared to say that she's your mother?'

'Would anyone with even an iota of self-respect be prepared to say that Viva King is his mother?'

'Quite apart from which,' said the Vicar, his pointed yet receding chin quivering like a divining rod, '*you* would probably claim that you'd got her in without her own identification and that you had therefore won the bet.'

The Vicar's receptionist returned.

'You may enter,' he said, giving the Vicar a card. 'My superior opines that military or clerical dress is acceptable without a tie.'

The Vicar and I made for the entrance to the first of the gaming rooms.

'So you won't help me out?' said Hamilton, his nose flattened and spread like a negro's.

'It's all your fault, what's happened,' said the Vicar over his shoulder: 'you shouldn't have encouraged that old woman to be so stupid.'

The Vicar and I turned into the enchanting rooms, on the beauty of which Flinny O'Flanagan had justly if unsoberly remarked fifteen years ago, built as they were on a gay and elegant Parisian model of the early 1800s.

'What did that receptionist mean about military dress?' I asked the Vicar. 'He said military dress would pass without a tie as well as clerical.'

'You should know. You were once a rorty soldier-boy. Surely mess jackets and so on are buttoned or fastened right up to the chin? Therefore no tie. Trust the Boche to make a special category for that.'

'My point is, Vicar, that nobody who is in the uniform of one of the armed services should be allowed in here at all. Officers, except in wartime, do *not* wear uniform when off duty.'

'What about common soldiers?'

'Surely the casino authorities would never admit a private?'

'The Germans are busy setting up their new democracy,' the Vicar instructed me. 'As you have just seen, they do everything according to regulation. Democratic regulation provides that where officers are admitted other ranks must be admitted, if they can afford a ticket.'

A Frenchman came past wearing tight trousers with spurs and a mess jacket buttoned up to the chin.

'At least he's an officer,' said the Vicar.

'How dare he appear in uniform when off parade?'

'The French don't know about that. They don't have proper officers, you see, they only have *officiers*, which is a very different thing. But this is the French zone, when all is said. One must try to tolerate French customs.'

The Vicar sat down in a vacant seat at the bottom of a roulette table, next to the croupier, who flinched. All occupants of the table, except for the croupiers, rose and withdrew.

'Ridiculous people,' said the Vicar. 'They think a gambling clergyman will bring them bad luck.'

'There is a scene in a book by Dennis Wheatley in which a canon goes to a casino in full canonicals. It turns out that he has sold his soul to the Devil. Perhaps these people think that you have.'

'Rubbish. They won't have read Dennis Wheatley.'

'Possibly they just disapprove.'

'Even Germans should be capable of minding their own business.'

The Vicar placed a German bank note of huge denomination in front of the croupier. '*Monnaie par dix marks*,' he said. The croupier scowled but passed the note up to the top of the table, to the two croupiers by the wheel, on the end of his rake. Two enormous piles of chips were pushed back. The croupier set them in front of the Vicar and withdrew his hands with a gesture of distaste, as if afraid of contamination.

'You've annoyed him by speaking French,' I said. 'You speak perfectly sound German, so why — '

' — All croupiers are supposed to respond to all civilised languages. I was just testing him. Anyway, it's not that which has annoyed him. It's

158

the defection of all the players from this table. There'll be less people to tip him if they win.'

'Only one person. You.'

'And I don't tip croupiers on principle,' the Vicar said, 'no matter how much I win. They are paid quite well enough without that.'

The Vicar made the first of a long series of winning bets and I made the first of my losing ones. After a shorter time than I had expected, Hamilton came in with Viva.

'In the end they let Viva in without her passport,' said Hamilton nonchalantly; 'that's why we're here so soon.'

'No, it is not,' said Viva, who was truthful to the point of pain, except when talking of her relations with famous or titled people. 'Hamilton rang up the hotel, and they sent the hotel car down with it, surprisingly quickly. *That's* why we're here so soon.'

'Well tried, Hamilton,' said the Vicar, then bent once more over the green baize.

'The Vicar's winning,' I said. 'No one else will play at this table because gamblers think vicars at the roulette table bring bad luck.'

'It's not that at all,' said Viva. 'They dislike vicars who are obviously Jews. "What is that Jew doing got up as a clergyman of the Church of England?" they are thinking to themselves. "He should be whamming his napper against the Wailing Wall." '

'I've forgotten to bring my money,' Hamilton said. 'Please lend me some of your winnings, Vicar.'

With an ill grace the Vicar lent him the equivalent of twenty-five pounds.

Hamilton now played that most contemptible of all games – following the bets of someone in luck. Instantly the Vicar started to lose; whereupon I myself, since I was backing totally different numbers and combinations, began to win.

'Lend me some more,' said Hamilton to the Vicar.

'No.'

'Simon?'

'All right. So long as you don't follow my bets. Or the Vicar's any more.'

But both the Vicar and I had exhausted our lucky streaks. Hamilton began to win. He was greedy, increased his stake, and still won.

'Right,' said the Vicar. He helped himself to half of Hamilton's last heap of winnings. 'A twenty-five pound loan,' he said, 'at today's rate of exchange as printed in the *Badener Tageblatte*, plus a hundred for that bet.'

'Right,' I said, and helped myself to the other half of Hamilton's heap.

Hamilton now lost the rest of his gains and produced some English notes to change for more counters.

'You said you hadn't any money with you,' said the Vicar.

'Only English money,' equivocated Hamilton.

'You borrowed from them because you hoped they'd forget,' said Viva, who had not forgiven Hamilton his failure to get her in without her passport; for like all obstinate people Viva particularly deprecated slights to her *amour-propre*.

'You're all turning against me,' said Hamilton, and sniffed ominously.

I remembered the present he had given me. It was, as I have said, well-chosen – chosen with understanding and with love, as I am vain about my hands; it was of high quality and very expensive.

'No need to change any English money,' I said. 'They'll only cheat you over the rate. Have what you need of mine.'

There was always something about Hamilton, always something he had said or done, that turned me as feeble as a jelly when he was upset; however much he deserved to be, and although I knew very well that in any given case he was only putting it on.

He now grabbed (I use the word advisedly) about one hundred and fifty pounds' worth of the counters in front of me and very swiftly lost them. He scowled as if the table had delivered a personal affront. He charged out of the rooms, charged back in to borrow the taxi fare to the hotel; 'Taxi-drivers won't take pound notes,' did not ask Viva whether she wanted to leave (instead of hanging about while the Vicar and I were still playing) and noisily departed.

Departed for good, as it turned out. Scared lest he might have to pay some part of Viva's hotel bill, or lest I might ask for my one hundred and fifty pounds' worth of Deutschmarks back, he took a night flight from Strasbourg to London, leaving a note which we found on our return to say that he was bored with the lot of us.

Needless to say, I never had my money back. Whenever I asked for it in London, he made infantile gestures and skipped out of the room. But I went on liking him, or at least enjoying him. Hamilton – it was his great gift – was eminently enjoyable.

Note. Later on that evening in the casino, after Hamilton had gone, the Vicar and I, having again picked up a bit at roulette, went to play at the Chemin-de-fer table, where two seats had just been left vacant. But the other seven players, whether they truly believed vicars brought bad luck or, as Viva had suggested earlier, just did not like Jews who were also Anglican priests, threatened to leave if the Vicar sat down. In the end, Viva had to sit in what would have been his place and play by his instruction. She was so dim that when it was her turn to play on behalf of the other punters against the banker, she drew a card instead of standing – despite an incisive order, twice repeated, from the Vicar – and lost the equivalent of about seventeen hundred pounds, which the punters would otherwise have won. According to the regulations, anyone who does this (it is called a '*faux tirage*'), has to reimburse his fellow punters; an obligation which now fell to the Vicar. The casino accountants accepted a cheque drawn on the Vicar's London bank (one of the fancy ones) but only after ringing up his bishop, the bank being of course closed at one-thirty a.m., to enquire after the Vicar's financial circumstances.

When the Vicar arrived home, the bishop sent for him and said that he himself had never seen any reason why clergymen shouldn't gamble and hunt and do everything else that other gentlemen did in the normal course. After all, said the Bishop, they had in the eighteenth century when everything was much better ordered than now. But what the kind old man did draw the line at was clerical dress in the gaming rooms. To wear it at the tables was discourteous and embarrassing to other people present, just as it would have been if the Vicar had worn it in a bordel or a night club. However, the bishop went on, he would forgive the Vicar this solecism, provided his point was taken and well remembered, if only because he had been asked out to dine most agreeably all over London in order to repeat the story of the Vicar's sermon about the TUC.

Given such a sensible and tolerant superior, one would have thought that even the Vicar could not go wrong, but alas . . . At this point words fail me, and I can only say that the Vicar has now been 'resting' for some years and is likely to continue so.

Second Note. Viva King died not so very long ago. She was unloved by me but, to be fair, is much missed by Hamish and the Vicar. She left her pictures to a Battle of Britain pilot who had had a sex change operation. The story is that the pilot became so impatient for his/her inheritance, although the pictures were worth almost nothing, that he/she climbed into Viva's house by ladder and stole them while Viva was expiring.

PART SIX

Studies In Conversion

i) The Ghetto

'There is a notable ghetto here in Prague,' Benjamin Crud said. 'They have turned the synagogue into a museum.'

'I'm game,' I said.

'I wish you would not use such expressions when we are discussing matters to do with Almighty God.'

' "*Deo injuriae, Dei curae.*" '

'You know we do not learn Latin in the States.'

' "Let God cope with His own wrongs." Let Him take his own revenge if He wants any.'

'Although that might serve you right,' said Crud, 'Christian charity as well as personal regard prompts me to hope that God will overlook your childish taunts. But if I were you I should not bait him.'

'The Christian God should show forbearance,' I said. 'He should do so of his own Christian charity without needing the addition of yours.'

'Being a Jew, I often confuse the Christian God of Love with the Jewish Jehovah, who delights in anger and vengeance.'

'If I were you,' I said, 'I should have stuck with Jehovah instead of being converted to the Lamb. The Lamb is painfully wet, whereas Jehovah's response of fury and denunciation is amply justified, by the behaviour of the Jews and everyone else. "After all," Jehovah might say, "the human race has poisoned my atmosphere and polluted my terrestrial creation simply in order that the lower classes may ride around in motor cars – having first destroyed the once exquisite countryside through which they ride and having also ruined everything to which it is worth riding." There is a lot to be said for the angry moods of Jehovah.'

It was the autumn of 1988. Benj Crud was now a converted member of the Roman Catholic Church. His manners were much improved but there were times when I thought his brain was softening.

'There is a remarkable cemetery in the ghetto,' Benj now said.

'As I've told you, I'm game.'

The Jewish cemetery in Prague had been so confined that the stones wriggled and jostled and wrestled against each other like the entire multitude of the world's dead all struggling to rise at the same time on the Last Day. Only here the stones were fighting not for air but for earth – for room in which to descend. No space was to be seen between the bases of tombs; where their shafts entered the ground they were so crammed and crowded and distorted that if you had tried to walk among them you would have been treading some six inches above the hidden surface of the soil with your shoes constantly wedged in the 'V's, or the upper part of the 'X's, formed by the angled slabs.

This was grotesque and rather disgusting: the museum was merely a bore, an endless nagging recitation of disease and massacre down the centuries. The lavatory under the entrance lodge smelt worse than any I had so far come across in Eastern Europe.

'Orthodox Jews don't like clearing up after Gentiles,' Benj said when I commented on this.

'They might just chuck a bit of Jeyes fluid about.'

'They probably can't get it behind the Iron Curtain. *We* can get pretty well what we want because we have hard currency. Czechoslovakians – Jewish or other – can get nothing.'

'I sometimes wonder why we came.'

'To see the Architecture and the Art,' Benj said: 'nobody could want to see the people.'

'They look as if they know it.'

'They have a long history of resignation.'

'Punctuated,' I said, 'by outbursts of violence.'

'Outbursts. Never sustained enough, or well enough organised, to free them from those that have enslaved them at any particular time.'

Now we were walking by the river. Shabby men and women sat

dismally on seats. Gaily dressed and immaculately behaved children were herded towards the opera house.

'Why are those children so smart?'

'There is a government subsidy for the clothes of children up to twelve years of age,' Benj said. 'It is well conceived. People will endure anything if they can look at their children and say, "How healthy and happy they are." '

Quite apart from their stylish apparel, the children that were being taken to see the opera house did indeed appear vigorous and contented.

'There are those that say,' said Benj Crud, 'that special squads of wholesome and well-fed children are trained and disciplined, and then paraded on the streets of Prague to impress tourists like us. In provincial towns, they say, you will see only undernourished children. Even their subsidised clothes cannot give them any appeal.'

'Do you believe that?'

'We have driven through several provincial towns. How have the children appeared to you?'

'Undernourished and sullen. Like everybody else.'

'That's why they make it so difficult for one to bring one's own car in. Charabancs stick to recommended routes . . . whereas those with their own cars can nose about where they're not wanted.'

'That reminds me,' I said. 'We are nearly out of fuel. Have you yet discovered where one can buy unleaded petrol?'

'Our Concierge tells me,' said Benj, 'that there is only one garage that sells it in the whole of Prague. On the other side of the river, in the middle of what he calls a suburban slum area. I do not think he will last much longer if he uses phrases like that.'

'Perhaps he too is specially trained – to impress on tourists a false notion of the demotic candour tolerated under the regime?'

'Whichever way one looks at it,' said Benj the convert, 'Prague is not a city that inspires one with Christian Charity.'

Back early that evening in our hotel of over a thousand rooms, in the suburbs but *not* the slummy ones where the garage was, Benj and I read aloud, as we often did for his edification and for my interest, a passage of the scriptures. At one time or another we had read Genesis, Job, the

Psalms and all four Gospels. Now it was the turn of the Acts of the Apostles. Since we took alternate chapters and I had won the toss to take the first, I now found myself landed with the fifth – the story of Ananias and his wife Sapphira. These two, you will doubtless recall, were part of a commune founded a short time after the Crucifixion by St Peter, governed by him and made up of devout Christians. Everyone was meant to put everything he had or made into the kitty for the common good, and all went well until Ananias sold a possession and kept back part of the price received. Somebody sneaked. St Peter summoned Ananias and charged him with lying 'not unto men, but unto God', and Ananias 'hearing these words fell down, and gave up the ghost'. The young men of the commune were then told to take away the cadaver and bury it. While they were thus employed, Sapphira came back from somewhere or other not knowing what had happened, was instantly accused of complicity in the sale, and had the grace to admit it; but St Peter went on nagging all the same – Why? How? etc. etc. – and then told her that the burial party which was presently disposing of Ananias 'shall carry thee out too'. At this Sapphira 'fell down straightaway at his feet' and 'yielded up the ghost'; as nasty a piece of intimidation as I know of; and the young men who had just returned had to go without their well-earned supper and take her away as well. A pause being indicated in the text at this juncture, I had a drink and a laugh and elaborated to Benj on my vision of the wretched young men dashing in and out with corpses like the Keystone Cops.

Benj was not amused. How dare I make mock of 'HOLY *WRIT*'? Could I not understand the significance of Ananias' and Sapphira's being 'blasted by God in his righteous anger'? I replied that there was no mention of God's blasting anyone in righteous anger, just of two people who had fatally succumbed to the bullying of St Peter – bullying which, in Sapphira's case, was wholly uncalled for. As for the thing being 'HOLY *WRIT*', this was neither here nor there and certainly no guarantee of truth; but this much, I conceded, could be said for the author of the book: that he had penned, whether intentionally or not, a ripe piece of comedy. The instant collapse, *zonk*, of the two avaricious parties was superb slapstick, and their hugger-mugger interment by the young disciples with Sapphira being summarily tipped on top of her husband – 'Take aim, dears, *whoops*' – appealed to my sense of the ridiculous. One could only hope, I said, that the amateur undertakers were given a good nosh when at last they were allowed one.

It was clear, said Benj, that I was no longer a fit person with whom to read the Bible – 'the word of *Ga-a-a-ad*' – and from now on we would read something else instead. Like *Hiawatha*. I remarked that as he had apparently lost both his wits and his sense of humour, commodities which he had possessed in some abundance before his conversion to the Romish superstition, *Hiawatha* would be most unsuitable. For since he could no longer either recognise or laugh at absurdity, the only conceivable pleasure to be had from the poem was beyond him. Let us, I suggested, read *Paradise Lost*, which contained an informative, if rather highly coloured, description of the Hell of which he was now sweating in fear.

He did not speak to me until lunch-time the next day; but my suggestion of reading *Paradise Lost*, of which I had a copy with me, was later adopted with considerable success. Although not much of a whizz at scanning iambic pentameters, a deficiency doubtless attributable to his education 'in the States', he relished the vanity and stupidity of Eve, who reminded him of his mother and his sister, and he was the only person I have ever known to find some attraction in Milton's dreary rendering of God in His Heaven.

ii) The Elephant

Although Benj Crud's intelligence had totally ceased to operate in matters of theology or religion, he did retain a certain shrewdness in secular affairs. From Prague we had driven to Dresden and from Dresden we planned to drive on to Weimar. In Weimar, Benj was determined to stay in the Elephant Hotel – an inn of historical standing (see Thomas Mann's uniquely boring novel, *Lottie in Weimar*) and, he had been told, of culinary merit. A booking was therefore made through reception at our hotel in Dresden.

'However,' said the obliging young lady at reception, 'you must confirm this booking through the Tourist Bureau here in Dresden tomorrow morning.'

Why must we confirm it?

Because, we were told, tourist visas in East Germany were conditional on tourists being securely booked into suitable hotels every night of their stay; and since we were staying an extra night to visit Weimar, the authorities must be told exactly where if they were to extend our visas . . . which would be inspected and stamped by 'the official lady at the Tourist Bureau'.

Since the Bureau was only fifty yards from the hotel, and since this kind of interference still had to be expected in this kind of country in 1988, we took the receptionist's instruction in good part and good faith . . . until, on arrival at the Tourist Bureau soon after it opened the next morning, we were interviewed by an obese and heavily moustached female with brittle hair which revealed patches of scabby scurf. She rather resembled Ian Fleming's immortal creation, Colonel Kleb (the toes of whose shoes, you will remember, when tapped on the ground in a certain way, emitted poisonous steel flanges).

'It is impossible,' said Kleb, 'that you go to the Hotel Elephant in Weimar.'

'We have already had our booking accepted,' said Benj.

'Not accepted by me. You go to the Red Star Hotel. Most suitable for you. Newly built for tourists.'

Benj looked at the map in his guidebook.

'Newly built in the suburbs,' he said: 'I wish to be in the centre. Why can we not go to the Elephant, which has already made a reservation for us?'

'Because there is now to be a conference there. No room left.'

'The receptionist of the Elephant knew of no conference last night.'

'She will know now. The hotel must be kept clear in case of Party Conference.'

'But — '

' — If you wish me to stamp your visas for one more night,' said Kleb, 'you will first pay me to spend that night at the Red Star Hotel.'

'American Express all right?'

'I suppose yes,' said Kleb with loathing.

As we drove along the disintegrating autobahn towards Weimar, Benj said: 'I don't believe in that conference.'

'It's the kind of wretched affair that everyone is always having these days. Particularly socialists and communists. Why else should she want to change our booking?'

'Because she's a horrible woman who enjoys exercising power over people.'

'Charity, Benjamin, charity . . .'

'What has she done to deserve any?'

'Perhaps,' I said, 'the Party has a special interest in the new hotel. A new venture which they want to get off to a good start. That kind of thing.'

'I am not to be inconvenienced by any preference of the Party's. What we shall do, dear boy,' said Benj, 'is go straight to the Elephant, find out if they are really booked solid for a conference. If not, we shall book in once more.'

'The penalties for defying that tyrannosaurus woman could be quite appalling.'

'Not to an American citizen,' said Benj, 'nor even to an English one.'

'Thank you for not saying "Brit". The trouble is that we've already paid for the Red Star in advance.'

'No, we haven't. I only pretended to sign the American Express voucher. That foul woman was so busy gloating that she didn't notice.'

The Elephant was half-empty, with no conference anywhere in sight. They would be delighted to have us.

'Why were we told you were full,' asked Benj, 'by the Tourist Bureau in Dresden?'

The young man at the desk pursed his lips as if about to kiss Benj; then stuck his tongue out and waggled it.

'The Touritht Bureau in Drethden is doubtleth wun by a Party Member. Party Memberth do not like hotelth of ethtablithed dithtincthion. They conthider them to be elititht.'

We walked round some of Weimar to get up an appetite for the thelebrated cuithine of the Elephant. Weimar was an unattractive town, scruffy, smelly, with few shops and those closed; the whole place was as scabby as Kleb's scalp, except for some newly cleaned public buildings. These imposed themselves but were not of themselves imposing. There seemed to be a lot of musical schools and colleges, according to the inscriptions carved above the gates, all of which were at present serving, according to fiercely printed posters stuck on the walls, as welfare or remedial centres of the Honneker administration.

After this depressing expedition, Benj's scansion of Milton's lines was even more than usually cretinous. He broke off half-way through the miraculous invocation at the beginning of Book III of *Paradise Lost*, 'Yet not the more/Cease I to wander where the Muses haunt', saying that he was feeling guilty about deceiving Kleb and must now pray to his '*Ga-a-a-ad*' to forgive him. I left as he sank theatrically to his knees. Dinner, in the most expensive of the Elephant's three World Famouth

Rethtaurantth was more nauseating than I should have thought possible.

No question of it: KLEB *VICTRIX*.

'At least,' said Benj after we had been allowed through the last of the six or seven barriers between East and West Germany, 'one now knows never to go there again. Thank God the East Germans are shut away from the rest of the world, even if we still have to cope with the brutes who live here in the West.'

'Nobody forced us to come,' I said; 'but your point is well taken.'

'You know,' said Benj, 'we owe a great debt of gratitude to the communists for keeping so many people behind the Iron Curtain and stopping them from cluttering up the more agreeable parts of Europe.'

'One does indeed. But perhaps they'll all be freed one day.'

'And then look out,' said Benj. 'People think that if they're freed, they'll be so happy and thankful that they'll do exactly what we tell them and behave like little lambkins. In fact they'll start up all the rows and riots and potty little sects and nationalisms that plagued Europe between the wars.'

'Balkanisation?'

'Balticisation too. And that's not all,' said Benj with righteous indignation. 'They'll blackmail the rest of Europe into paying to put their filthy polluted countries and bankrupt economies in order *and* into raising their standards of living. Interest will rise and the effect will rub right off on the citizens of the United States.'

'Another thing,' I said. 'What will they do with their secret police and so on? They can't just gas the whole lot.'

'It's not just the secret police,' said Benj. 'The only people in those wretched commie countries capable of running anything remotely difficult or complicated will be commies trained to do so, however badly. If they kick them out of their posts, the country in question collapses. If they leave them in their posts, the country remains communist right under the skin.'

'With all the old horrors liable to be resurrected at any moment?' I said.

'Yes. And now I come to think of it, that's the best thing we can hope for. We must hope and pray,' said Benjamin Crud, 'that if ever the countries behind the Curtain do get rid of communism, it will come slinking back through the postern gate, so to speak, and reimpose the old regime – so that at least their people aren't going to be slouching and whining and begging all over the West.'

'Would this be the orthodox Christian line?' I enquired.

'Communists are the enemies of Christ. It is not required of Christians to tolerate their nuisance.'

'We are talking about their subjects – their victims. And even in regard to the communists themselves, Christians are enjoined to turn the other cheek and to forgive unto seventy times seven.'

'The danger is,' said Benj, ignoring this, 'that once people are allowed to leave those disgusting places, they are going to zoom right out and not let themselves be cajoled back in a hurry.'

'So that they will go on slouching and whining and begging, as you so eloquently put it, all over the West? Luckily quite a lot of them are numb with poverty and discipline – *and*, don't forget, security of a kind; so that you may very well find that a majority of them stay in the East after all.'

'Yes. But by that time they'll have smelt prosperity and they'll be yelling for a hunk of it for themselves.'

'Hadn't you heard that we are entering on an era of caring and sharing?'

'Caring and sharing,' said Benj, 'kill prosperity dead.'

'That's the whole point of them,' I said: 'then no one will have anything to be envious about any more.'

'Is that what you want?'

'What I want, Benj, is to live on an island in a lake on another island in another lake on an atoll totally surrounded by sheer one thousand foot cliffs of marble, in the middle of the Ocean of Zembla, reading Homer, Virgil, Dante and Milton; with no radio, television or newspapers now or ever.'

'Would you have a Holy Bible?'

'Yes. Longwinded and contentious it may be, but it is, by and large, fine literature.'

'What about food and drink?'

'I'm only conjuring a fantasy. One cannot command a commissariat to provision a fantasy . . . least of all an elitist fantasy like this.'

We both sighed.

'Would you settle for a truly Christian world?' asked Benj.

'Not as envisaged by early Christians or by papists, with all that preaching and posturing and inquisition. I'd settle for a Christian world founded by the broad Church of England and ruled by Archdeacon Grantley and his father-in-law Canon Harding – the one that played the cello.'

'You underestimate us Catholics, you know. People enjoy being preachers and posturers and inquisitors,' said Benj. 'And more people than you might think enjoy being preached at and postured at and investigated. It makes them the centre of attention for a while.'

'And the subsequent torture?'

'Some, at least, regard it as morally remedial.'

'Come, come,' I said.

'I do,' said Benj.

A pause.

'I must know,' I said at length. 'Were you converted out of conviction? Or was the appeal what you pretty well admitted to me, that time in Torcello . . . on Midsummer's Eve?'

'What did I admit?'

'That you wanted Insurance. That you wanted to take out a Policy, with the oldest firm in the business, against the contingency of eternal damnation.'

'I was frightened,' said Benj.

'Frightened by God?'

'By what I had done to offend Him.'

'He Himself promises clemency,' I observed.

'Only if you recognise His Authority. And genuinely repent of your evil-doing.'

'Surely . . . you could have returned to your old Jewish God? Jealous Jahveh . . . Jehovah . . . may have been, but he would have forgiven your wickedness in return for your loyalty. His record shows that very clearly.'

'I had to reject Jewry as a matter of taste, dear boy. In the last resort,' said Benj, 'one cannot be doing with a religion which commands the aesthetic crime of circumcision.'

PART SEVEN

Conclusions

Conclusion (i)

'You must hear this, Simon,' Hamish said. 'Your attentions stifle me. Your mere presence is intolerable. You try to possess me, to move in on me, like a wandering ghost with no body of its own. So much for your Platonic love. It is an incursion, an irruption, a kind of spiritual rape. So although we shall remain friends before the world, we shall seldom see each other from now on. I am going to India, because it is a very large country and a very long way from you, in every conceivable sense.'

Conclusion (ii)

'Where shall we stop on the way home?' said O.

'Where we like. There is plenty of time. I had thought of Cahors and Millau. Then somewhere like Brantôme on the way north.'

'Wasn't there a man called "Brantôme"?'

'He was, I think, count of the place. He ended up as abbot of the monastery there. He did a deal with the Huguenots, to stop them sacking it.'

'Money?'

'No. Charm.'

'I never thought of him as an abbot. I thought he was a courtier and a gambler and a seducer – lots of amusing things like that.'

'He was. He wrote about them – about women in particular – with appreciation and wit. Then he got bored,' I said. 'He just didn't want any more of it.'

'In India,' said O, 'when a man of wealth and worldly fame reaches a certain age, he renders an account of his assets to his heir, then puts on the clothes of a beggar and wanders over the country, seeking to become a holy man. Was it like that with Brantôme?'

'No. What he wanted was peace and quiet. He wanted to cease from hustle.'

'That's what these Indians are after. If you give away everything, you need worry about nothing.'

'Brantôme wanted a different kind of peace. He wanted to be at leisure to sum up, without disruption or intrusion, the lessons of his worldly career, and to compare these lessons with those formulated by

188

others. He wanted the peace of a well-stocked library. These Indians you speak of want nullity. That is *their* idea of wisdom.'

'What I said they were seeking was "holiness".'

'Rather a long order.'

The little ripples lapped on the pebbles of the beach where we were having our picnic.

'The point about Brantôme,' I went on, 'at least as I see it, was that he wanted to draw up his conclusions about the world in an intelligent and civilised fashion. Those Indians of yours want to dispense with knowledge and intelligence; they want to merge with the eternal. They want to be absolved from the personal effort which is an essential part of being an individual, even an individual who has retired, like Brantôme, into a monastery.'

'You seem to be saying,' said O, 'that Europe and the West believe in private intellectual endeavour, whereas most Indians and Orientals just want to surrender to oblivion.'

'I'm saying just about that.'

'Like your friend, Hamish M'cSass, who's always going to India? Who never reads a book, you say, and is always blathering about meditation?'

'Rather like him,' I said. 'He hasn't exactly given away his worldly goods but it amuses him to pretend that he has none, not least as this excuses and assists his parsimony.'

'He gets a high out of not spending money?'

'You could put it like that.'

'And of course,' said O, 'it must be very economic to spend the whole day just meditating.'

'Oh yes. No cash needed – and little enough in the way of mental exertion. You just let your mind go blank.'

'Isn't that rather difficult?'

'Not if you're ignorant and ill-read. Like most Indians. And like Hamish. The difference is, of course, that Indians can't really help being in that condition, but Hamish can. He went to Cambridge; he has a very fair intelligence. He simply decided, at a very early age, that it was easier to find someone else – Hamilton – to carry him through life and pay for his treats, than to be his own man and make his own efforts.

The rest, from his youthful "marriage" to his middle-aged meditation, follows easily enough.'

'Aren't you being rather spiteful about Hamish?'

'Yes.'

'Why?' said O.

'Because he threw me over. I began to bore him and he threw me over. It is the duty of a true friend to put up with being bored. God knows, I had been bored enough by him over the years; but because I loved him in my way, I put up with it . . . as I did with his avarice, with the horrible companions whom he produced from time to time, and with his enormous conceit of his mediocre intellect and his fading beauty. Now that he has finally spurned what I have to offer, he has released me from any further obligation. Like Brantôme, I can retire to a well stocked library and compare the lessons which I have learned with those recorded by other and wiser men.'